D0473526

PREPARING FOR THE WORLD OF WORK

A WORKBOOK BY

FRANK C. ROSKOS

2001 Edition

Published by

F. R. PUBLICATIONS
1103 St. Paul Drive
Merrill, Wisconsin 54452

Phone (715) 536-2836

Table of Contents

TO THE STUDENT

This workbook was written for the student who is planning to enter the world of work. It gives the necessary information that a person must have to find and hold a job.

This workbook should be studied carefully now, and then put away to be used as a reference later in life. It would be a good idea to review it from time to time while on the job. If questions come up, the workbook may help you find the answers.

As you read the lessons and complete the exercises, remember that you should try to do the best work you can do. Just as you should try to do your best in school, you should try to do your best at your job. Remember that neither the teacher nor the workbook can learn for you. That is your job. In a very short period of time, you will be working on your own. What you learn here will be important to you later in life.

TO THE TEACHER

This workbook introduces the student to the vocabulary and information needed for an effective work-study program. It can also be used as a basic text to acquaint the student with essential information concerning the work-a-day world.

It may be helpful to read the lesson orally in class. This can be done by either the teacher or volunteer student readers. Immediately following the oral reading, the vocabulary exercise should be completed. The vocabulary exercise will give the student an understanding of the more difficult words, as well as an understanding of the employment vocabulary in the lesson.

After the vocabulary exercise is completed, it may be helpful to have the students reread the lesson either orally or silently. After the second reading, the student should be properly prepared to complete most of the remaining exercises in the lesson. Some of the career-related exercises may require teacher assistance. The difficult employment words used in the workbook are repeated many times in the reading and student exercises. Upon completion of the workbook, the student should be familiar with these words.

The above are only suggestions; no doubt individual creativity will find additional techniques for presenting this material.

LESSON 1. SOCIAL SECURITY

The Social Security Act was passed by the Congress of the United States in 1935. It was passed to give American workers protection during their working years and upon retirement. During the years that a person works, he/she pays money into a special trust fund held by the United States Government. This special fund is then used to provide income when the family earnings are reduced or stop because of retirement, disability, or death. Social Security is also known as F.I.C.A. insurance. Benefits are paid from these special funds in the following ways:

1. When a worker has reached retirement age, he/she may retire from the job. An individual will then get money from the government every month. This is known as "retirement income".

2. If a worker dies, monthly checks may go to certain members of the worker's family. A lump-sum payment may also be paid when a worker dies. This payment goes only to a widow or widower.

3. If a worker is disabled before retirement age (hurt or sick for a long period of time) and cannot work, he/she receives a monthly check from the government.

The employer keeps back, or withholds, a certain amount of money from a worker's wages for Social Security taxes. The employer will add an additional amount that is equal to the amount withheld from the worker's paycheck. In this way, the employer and the employee pay the same

1

amount. The two amounts are sent in to the government and placed in the Social Security account fund. If a person is self-employed, the total tax is paid when the federal income tax is paid.

The amount of payment or benefit that a worker and a family will receive will depend on the earnings over the years. The more money the worker has earned, the greater the benefits will be. Of course, more Social Security taxes will have been paid if there have been high earnings.

A part of a worker's Social Security tax goes into a hospital insurance fund. When a person reaches age sixty-five or is disabled, money from this fund helps pay the hospital bills. This insurance is known as "Medicare". Voluntary medical insurance is also available to people over sixty-five years of age and to certain disabled people. This insurance helps pay doctor bills and other medical expenses. People over sixty-five years of age and disabled people pay an extra monthly payment for the voluntary medical insurance.

Workers are covered by Social Security protection even if they change jobs or move to a different city or state. Nearly every job that a person might take is covered by Social Security. Most workers in the United States are covered by Social Security. A person is even covered while in the Armed Services.

Every employee is required to have a Social Security card. This card is the most important paper anyone will need for a job. The Social Security card is given to everyone who fills out the required form. This form is submitted to Social Security along with a birth certificate and some form of identification. If a person is age 18 or older and has never been assigned a number before, he/she must apply in person. There is no charge. The application form may be obtained from the nearest Social Security Office or the Internet.

In most cases Social Security cards are applied for soon after a child's birth. This enables the parents of the child to claim that child as a dependent on their tax return.

MATCHING: Match the words in Column 1 with the correct meaning in Column 2.

Column 1   Column 2

_____   1.   employee   A.   a sum of money set aside for a special purpose

_____   2.   employer   B.   a person or firm who hires others

_____   3.   self-employed   C.   hold back - keep back

_____   4.   dependent   D.   a person who is supported by another

_____   5.   trust fund   E.   give up occupation or job

_____   6.   retirement   F.   payments made from Social Security

_____   7.   withhold   G.   money received for work

_____   8.   benefits   H.   a person who works for some person or firm for pay

_____   9.   Congress   I.   a person who works for himself/herself

_____   10.   paycheck   J.   law-making body of the United States

DEFINE: Use the dictionary to define the following words.

1. obtained --

2. employment --

3. application --

4. occupation --

5. minimum --

TRUE OR FALSE: Place a "T" for true and "F" for false before each statement.

_____   1.   Congress passed the Social Security Act in 1935.

_____   2.   A worker's dependent family could receive Social Security benefits in case
              the worker died.

_____   3.   An employer does not pay any amount toward an employee's Social Security
              payment.

_____   4.   The Social Security tax for a self-employed person is paid when the federal
              income tax is paid.

_____   5.   A worker may receive Social Security benefits if disabled.

_____   6.   A Social Security tax is withheld from the worker's paycheck.

(continued)

_____ 7. Social Security taxes are paid during a worker's working years.

_____ 8. Social Security benefits depend on the amount of earnings during an employee's working years.

_____ 9. A worker's Social Security tax is the money used to pay his/her benefits after retirement.

_____ 10. The employee and employer share the payment of the Social Security tax.

_____ 11. An individual is covered by Social Security while in the Army.

_____ 12. If a person moves to a different city or state he/she must obtain a new Social Security card.

_____ 13. Voluntary medical insurance is used to pay doctor bills after age sixty-five.

_____ 14. If people are in business for themselves, they are covered by Social Security.

_____ 15. A worker's protection under Social Security will stop if the worker changes jobs.

_____ 16. Workers must be eighteen years old before they can get Social Security cards.

_____ 17. Social Security cards are free.

_____ 18. A person must be employed before applying for a Social Security card.

_____ 19. F.I.C.A. insurance is another name for Social Security.

_____ 20. The Social Security card is not needed for most jobs.

LETTERS: Fill in the missing letters.

1. de __ en __ ent	10. fu __ d	19. pr __ tect __ on
2. so __ i __ l	11. spe __ i ___ l	20. pay __ ent
3. be __ e __ its	12. pa __ ___ heck	21. ac __ ount
4. se __ uri __ y	13. em __ lo __ er	22. ad __ iti __ nal
5. re __ ire	14. di __ ab __ ed	23. e __ rni __ gs
6. co __ ered	15. pas __ ed	24. cer __ ain
7. hos __ ital	16. de __ uct	25. a __ ount
8. e __ploy __ d	17. with __ old	26. a __ plic __ tion
9. in __ uran __ e	18. vol __ nta __ y	27. em __ loy __ e

JOB SELECTION: Below are the names of four jobs in a row. Three of the jobs are the same, or nearly the same type of work. One of the jobs is different and does not go with the other three. Draw a line under the job that does not belong with the others.

Example: doctor   nurse   <u>farmer</u>   surgeon

1. baker	butcher	cook	dentist
2. rabbi	priest	florist	minister
3. delivery person	letter carrier	paper girl	mechanic
4. writer	truck driver	author	poet
5. carpenter	teacher	bricklayer	roofer
6. police officer	painter	electrician	plumber
7. cab driver	police officer	deputy	sheriff
8. soldier	banker	sailor	marine
9. cashier	teller	beautician	clerk
10. mason	stenographer	typist	secretary
11. nurse's aide	practical nurse	pipefitter	orderly
12. librarian	plasterer	bricklayer	mason

MISSING "O's": Following is a list of groups of letters. Each group will make a real word if one or two "O's" are added. Make a real word from each group of letters by adding one or two "O's".

Examples: zer -- zero   clr -- color   mn -- moon

1. wrk _____	5. amunt _____	9. ut _____
2. jb _____	6. scial _____	10. ft _____
3. lk _____	7. als _____	11. dctr _____
4. lng _____	8. ver _____	12. mve _____

MISSING "E's": In this group of letters, make a real word by adding one or two "E's".

Examples: rady -- ready   cntr -- center

1. rtir _____	5. wags _____	9. thy _____
2. giv _____	6. chck _____	10. vn _____
3. hld _____	7. vry _____	11. lttr _____
4. latr _____	8. tim _____	12. covr _____

WORDS: Fill in the blanks with the correct words.

Medicare   coverage   dependent

share   retire

1. Social Security hospital insurance is known as _____ .

2. A person receives _____ while serving in the armed forces.

3. The worker and the employer _____ the Social Security tax.

4. Workers may receive Social Security benefits when they _____.

5. In case a worker dies, the _____ family may receive Social Security benefits.

QUESTIONS:

1. List four benefits that could be paid under Social Security.

   1. _____

   2. _____

   3. _____

   4. _____

2. If a person is self-employed, how would Social Security taxes be paid?

   _____

   _____

   _____

3. When can a worker receive benefits under Social Security hospital insurance?

   _____

   _____

   _____

4. If a person is an employee, how would Social Security taxes be paid?

   _____

   _____

   _____

Below is a correctly filled out Social Security application form. Notice that all information is printed except the signature. The completed form is mailed to the nearest Social Security Administration Office.

Form Approved
OMB No. 0960-0066

SOCIAL SECURITY ADMINISTRATION Application for a Social Security Card

1	**NAME** TO BE SHOWN ON CARD →	First **Mark** Full Middle Name **James** Last **Adams**	
	FULL NAME AT BIRTH IF OTHER THAN ABOVE →	First Full Middle Name Last	
	OTHER NAMES USED →		

2	**MAILING ADDRESS** Do Not Abbreviate →	Street Address, Apt. No., PO Box, Rural Route No. **705 Oak Street**
		City **Goodrich** State **Michigan** Zip Code **49445**

3 CITIZENSHIP (Check One) →
☒ U.S. Citizen   ☐ Legal Alien Allowed To Work   ☐ Legal Alien Not Allowed To Work   ☐ Other (See Instructions On Page 1)

4 SEX →
☒ Male   ☐ Female

5 RACE/ETHNIC DESCRIPTION (Check One Only—Voluntary) →
☐ Asian Asian-American or Pacific Islander   ☐ Hispanic   ☐ Black (Not Hispanic)   ☐ North American Indian or Alaskan Native   ☒ White (Not Hispanic)

6 DATE OF BIRTH   **10-26-20··**   Month, Day, Year
7 PLACE OF BIRTH (Do Not Abbreviate)   **Goodrich Michigan**   City / State or Foreign Country   FCI   Office Use Only

8 A. MOTHER'S MAIDEN NAME → First **Jane**   Full Middle Name **Ann**   Last Name At Her Birth **Meyer**
B. MOTHER'S SOCIAL SECURITY NUMBER (Complete only if applying for a number for a child under age 18.) → ③ ⑨ ⑨ - ⓪ ⓪ - ⓪ ⓪ ⓪ ⓪

9 A. FATHER'S NAME → First **James**   Full Middle Name **David**   Last **Adams**
B. FATHER'S SOCIAL SECURITY NUMBER (Complete only if applying for a number for a child under age 18.) → ③ ⑨ ⑧ - ⓪ ⓪ - ⓪ ⓪ ⓪ ⓪

10 Has the applicant or anyone acting on his/her behalf ever filed for or received a Social Security number card before?
☐ Yes (If "yes", answer questions 11-13.)   ☒ No (If "no", go on to question 14.)   ☐ Don't Know (If "don't know", go on to question 14.)

11 Enter the Social Security number previously assigned to the person listed in item 1. → ☐☐☐-☐☐-☐☐☐☐

12 Enter the name shown on the most recent Social Security card issued for the person listed in item 1. → First / Middle / Last

13 Enter any different date of birth if used on an earlier application for a card. → _____ Month, Day, Year

14 TODAY'S DATE   **1-15-20··**   Month, Day, Year
15 DAYTIME PHONE NUMBER   **(616) 555-9009**   Area Code / Number

DELIBERATELY FURNISHING (OR CAUSING TO BE FURNISHED) FALSE INFORMATION ON THIS APPLICATION IS A CRIME PUNISHABLE BY FINE OR IMPRISONMENT, OR BOTH.

16 YOUR SIGNATURE ► *Mark James Adams*
17 YOUR RELATIONSHIP TO THE PERSON IN ITEM 1 IS:
☒ Self   ☐ Natural or Adoptive Parent   ☐ Legal Guardian   ☐ Other (Specify)

DO NOT WRITE BELOW THIS LINE (FOR SSA USE ONLY)

NPN		DOC	NTI	CAN	ITV
PBC	EVI EVA	EVC	PRA	NWR DNR	UNIT

EVIDENCE SUBMITTED

SIGNATURE AND TITLE OF EMPLOYEE(S) REVIEWING EVIDENCE AND/OR CONDUCTING INTERVIEW

DATE

DCL   DATE

Form **SS-5** Internet (2-98) Destroy Prior Editions

Fill out the following Social Security card application form carefully. Answer all questions just as you would if you were applying for your card.

SOCIAL SECURITY ADMINISTRATION Application for a Social Security Card

Form Approved
OMB No. 0960-0066

		First	Full Middle Name	Last
1	**NAME** TO BE SHOWN ON CARD →			
	FULL NAME AT BIRTH IF OTHER THAN ABOVE → (First)	(Full Middle Name)	(Last)	
	OTHER NAMES USED →			

		Street Address, Apt. No., PO Box, Rural Route No.		
2	**MAILING ADDRESS** → Do Not Abbreviate	City	State	Zip Code

3 CITIZENSHIP (Check One) →
☐ U.S. Citizen   ☐ Legal Alien Allowed To Work   ☐ Legal Alien Not Allowed To Work   ☐ Other (See Instructions On Page 1)

4 SEX → ☐ Male   ☐ Female

5 RACE/ETHNIC DESCRIPTION (Check One Only—Voluntary) →
☐ Asian Asian-American or Pacific Islander   ☐ Hispanic   ☐ Black (Not Hispanic)   ☐ North American Indian or Alaskan Native   ☐ White (Not Hispanic)

6 DATE OF BIRTH ____ Month, Day, Year   **7** PLACE OF BIRTH (Do Not Abbreviate) ____ City ____ State or Foreign Country   FCI   Office Use Only

8	**A. MOTHER'S MAIDEN NAME** →	First	Full Middle Name	Last Name At Her Birth
	B. MOTHER'S SOCIAL SECURITY NUMBER (Complete only if applying for a number for a child under age 18.) →	☐☐☐ – ☐☐ – ☐☐☐☐		

9	**A. FATHER'S NAME** →	First	Full Middle Name	Last
	B. FATHER'S SOCIAL SECURITY NUMBER (Complete only if applying for a number for a child under age 18.) →	☐☐☐ – ☐☐ – ☐☐☐☐		

10 Has the applicant or anyone acting on his/her behalf ever filed for or received a Social Security number card before?

☐ Yes (If "yes", answer questions 11-13.)   ☐ No (If "no", go on to question 14.)   ☐ Don't Know (If "don't know", go on to question 14.)

11 Enter the Social Security number previously assigned to the person listed in item 1. → ☐☐☐ – ☐☐ – ☐☐☐☐

12 Enter the name shown on the most recent Social Security card issued for the person listed in item 1. → First   Middle   Last

13 Enter any different date of birth if used on an earlier application for a card. → ____ Month, Day, Year

14 TODAY'S DATE ____ Month, Day, Year   **15** DAYTIME PHONE NUMBER (____) ____ Area Code   Number

DELIBERATELY FURNISHING (OR CAUSING TO BE FURNISHED) FALSE INFORMATION ON THIS APPLICATION IS A CRIME PUNISHABLE BY FINE OR IMPRISONMENT, OR BOTH.

16 YOUR SIGNATURE ▶   **17** YOUR RELATIONSHIP TO THE PERSON IN ITEM 1 IS:
☐ Self   ☐ Natural or Adoptive Parent   ☐ Legal Guardian   ☐ Other (Specify)

DO NOT WRITE BELOW THIS LINE (FOR SSA USE ONLY)					
NPN		DOC	NTI	CAN	ITV
PBC	EVI	EVA	EVC	PRA	NWR	DNR	UNIT
EVIDENCE SUBMITTED				SIGNATURE AND TITLE OF EMPLOYEE(S) REVIEWING EVIDENCE AND/OR CONDUCTING INTERVIEW	
					DATE
				DCL	DATE

Form **SS-5** Internet (2-98) Destroy Prior Editions

LESSON 2. REASONS PEOPLE WORK

There are many reasons why people work. One person may work for one reason and another person for another. If one were to ask someone why he/she worked, his/her first answer might be, "to earn money". While this may be true for many people, there are some rich people who also work very hard. They surely do not need the money. They must work for other reasons.

Although people work for many reasons, some of the more important reasons are as follows:

1. Earning Money

Most people need to work to make a living. In the days of the pioneers when each family raised its own food, cut its own firewood, made its own clothes, and built its own home, there was less need for money. Today we depend on other people to do these jobs. Therefore, it is necessary to earn money to buy the things that are needed and wanted. Some of the things that are bought are necessary for life and others add happiness and enjoyment to life.

It should be remembered that the amount of money a person earns from an employer will depend on what the worker has to offer the employer. The more valuable a service, product, or benefit that can be provided, the more the employer will be able to pay.

2. Security

It is only natural that people are somewhat worried about the future. Most people are concerned about how long they will be able to keep their jobs or what might happen to them and their families if they were unable to work. Sometimes workers say they are saving a "nest egg" for the future. This means they are putting aside some money for future use. A savings account at a bank or buying Government Savings Bonds would be examples of a "nest egg". The worker might say that the money saved is for a "rainy day". This means that the savings could be used when the worker is out of work or is ill for a long period of time. The reason people buy insurance of all kinds is that they are concerned about the future. Work that is done today may provide money that can be used in the future. Therefore, some people work to provide this security.

3.   Gaining Experience

Sometimes people work at a job so that they can gain some experience and get a better job. A person might start out as a dishwasher in a restaurant. A good worker will gain experience on the job and might move up to a cook's helper in the kitchen. Work is necessary so he/she can gain experience on the job. This experience may help a person become a more valuable employee and provide a chance for advancement on the job.

4.   Feeling Important

All people like to feel they are needed. This gives a purpose to life. Many times one hears the saying, "He wanted to make something of himself." Many people can make something of themselves through work. Work by one person provides a service or product for another person.

People belong to clubs and organizations because it makes them feel important. Doing a good job at work can also make one feel important. If people take pride in their work, they may find it a very enjoyable part of their lives. Hearing the words "good job" makes most people feel very good.

5. Achievement

Most men and women want to achieve something during their lives. Working provides a way for them to get the things they want out of life. It is important for workers to set some goals for their future work. Workers should know what they want to achieve and then set out to achieve it.

6. Recognition

All people like to receive credit for what they do. From the time they are small children they like to be told they are doing a good job. Receiving credit and recognition for doing good work makes anyone feel good. It also makes people try to work harder and do better. Next to the need to earn a living, perhaps the reason most people work is to receive some form of recognition.

7. Social Value

The work that a person does is valuable to society. The work that a doctor does not only benefits the doctor, but helps the people who are treated. The work that the waitress in a restaurant does, provides a service to each of the customers. Without the farmer, there would be no food to eat. Without the work of people, the world, as it is today, could not exist. Each day everyone benefits from the job that others do. Some, who do not need the money, work for the benefit of others without pay. A person may work very hard to help a neighbor who is ill or handicapped. Many times, people work to aid those who have been harmed by floods, hurricanes, fires, or earthquakes. Some also volunteer much time and money to help such organizations as the Community Chest, United Way, or Red Cross.

8. Keeping Busy

Many times people complain about their work and how much they have to do. They say it would be better to relax and take it easy rather than work. But the fact remains that without work, some people would find it difficult to find enough to do. Work provides an outlet for their energy. There are times when older workers would prefer not to retire. Their jobs give them a chance to keep busy. It is easy to see that finding a job and doing that job to the best of one's ability, is an important part of life. People work for many different reasons, from wanting money to helping others. Since so much of adult life is spent working, it is important to study the world of work and choose a job carefully.

MATCHING: Match the words in Column 1 with the correct meaning in Column 2.

Column 1   Column 2

_____ 1.   enjoyment   A. worth something

_____ 2.   service   B. practice; knowledge gained by doing things

_____ 3.   valuable   C. promotion; move ahead; go up

_____ 4.   security   D. goods produced as a result of work

_____ 5.   natural   E. pleasure; joy

_____ 6.   experience   F. gain by effort; get done

_____ 7.   advancement   G. giving attention to; show appreciation

_____ 8.   pride   H. something that is desired; something to get in
                                      the future

_____ 9.   achieve
                                  I. work for others; for benefit of others
_____ 10. products
                                  J. high opinion of one's worth or possessions;
_____ 11. recognition   being proud

_____ 12. goal   K. feeling of being safe

                                  L. produced by nature; coming in the regular
                                      course of events

MULTIPLE CHOICE: Select the one best answer.

_____ 1.   Saving for a "rainy day" means --

              A. putting money aside for a time when a person cannot work
              B. putting money aside for days when it is cloudy
              C. putting money aside to pay Social Security taxes

_____ 2.   When people work on a job for a period of time, they are gaining --

              A. product on the job
              B. experience on the job
              C. direction on the job

_____ 3.   Work by one person may provide --

              A. pay for another person
              B. a product for another person
              C. a goal for another person

_____ 4.   Moving up from a dishwasher to a cook's helper is known as --

              A. security   B. recognition   C. advancement

_____ 5.   Receiving credit for what a person has done is known as --

              A. a "nest egg"   B. experience   C. recognition

COMPOUND WORDS: The word carport was formed by joining together the words <u>car</u> and <u>port</u>. Match the words from Column 1 with the words from Column 2 to form a new word in Column 3.

Column 1	Column 2	Column 3
1. with	A. what	1. _____
2. some	B. out	2. _____
3. some	C. fore	3. _____
4. earth	D. check	4. _____
5. with	E. quake	5. _____
6. there	F. washer	6. _____
7. her	G. selves	7. _____
8. them	H. hold	8. _____
9. dish	I. self	9. _____
10. pay	J. time	10. _____

JOB SELECTION: Below are the names of four jobs in a row. Three of the jobs are the same, or nearly the same type of work. One of the jobs is different and does not go with the other three. Draw a line under the job that does not go with the others.

Example: carpenter   <u>salesperson</u>   roofer   plasterer

1. butler	welder	bellhop	porter
2. mortician	molder	hammersmith	die maker
3. chef	baker	bus driver	cook
4. disc jockey	logger	announcer	newsperson
5. painter	dairyworker	paperhanger	plasterer
6. manicurist	barber	beautician	computer operator
7. sailor	mortician	embalmer	funeral director
8. jeweler	herdsperson	dairyworker	cattle rancher
9. tool designer	logger	forester	lumberworker
10. principal	taxi driver	teacher	guidance counselor
11. maid	electrician	housekeeper	domestic worker
12. messenger	usher	bellhop	cheesemaker
13. watchperson	doorperson	accountant	guard

13

TRUE or **FALSE**: Place a "T" for true and "F" for false before each statement.

_____ 1. Most people need to work to make a living.

_____ 2. Earning money is more important today than it was during the time of the pioneers.

_____ 3. The only reason people work is to earn money.

_____ 4. Rich people do not work.

_____ 5. A savings account at a bank is putting money aside for the future.

_____ 6. When people work, they provide a product or service for other people.

_____ 7. One of the reasons people work is to receive recognition.

_____ 8. The amount of money earned from an employer depends on what service, product, or benefit the employee can offer the employer.

_____ 9. Experience on a job is of no value.

_____ 10. Work can give purpose to life.

MATCHING JOBS: Listed below is one column of jobs and one column of products or services. Match the job with the product or service that is performed.

	Jobs		**Services or Products**
_____	1. bookkeeper	A.	installs pipes
_____	2. teacher	B.	plants crops
_____	3. farmer	C.	splices cable
_____	4. draftsman	D.	washes clothes
_____	5. janitor	E.	instructs students
_____	6. shipping clerk	F.	skids logs
_____	7. plumber	G.	prepares scale drawings
_____	8. carpenter	H.	makes shoes
_____	9. minister	I.	ships merchandise
_____	10. telephone line worker	J.	sweeps floors
_____	11. auto mechanic	K.	sells cars
_____	12. laundry worker	L.	keeps records
_____	13. salesperson	M.	repairs cars
_____	14. assembly-line worker	N.	preaches sermons
_____	15. forestry worker	O.	builds homes
_____	16. pharmacist	P.	sells drugs

PRODUCT MATCHING: Column 1 has a list of names of companies that manufacture products. In Column 2 is a list of the products they manufacture. Match the product with the company.

Column 1

Company

_____ 1. Northern Door Corporation

_____ 2. Gardner Baking Company

_____ 3. Weber Publishing Company

_____ 4. Acme Dairy Company

_____ 5. Johnson Pottery Corporation

_____ 6. Atlas Lock Corporation

_____ 7. Case Implement Corporation

_____ 8. Sandknit Sportswear, Inc.

_____ 9. Parker Pen Corporation

_____ 10. Seamless Hosiery Corporation

_____ 11. Midwest Drug Corporation

_____ 12. Leonard Building Products, Inc.

_____ 13. Clark Oil Refiners, Inc.

_____ 14. Blue Bird Cutlery Company

_____ 15. Krass Bottling, Inc.

_____ 16. Lincoln Canning Company

_____ 17. Eagle Luggage, Inc.

_____ 18. Page Drapery Studios, Inc.

_____ 19. Van's Packing, Inc.

_____ 20. M & J Plumbing Company

_____ 21. A & L Electric Company

_____ 22. Taylor Insulation Company

_____ 23. Valley Marble & Granite, Inc.

_____ 24. Butterfield Refrigeration, Inc.

Column 2

Product

A. ice cream

B. house curtains

C. football helmets

D. doughnuts

E. knives

F. stockings

G. soft drinks

H. garage doors

I. summer sausage

J. school books

K. aspirin

L. suitcases

M. clay vases

N. kitchen sinks

O. house siding

P. pencils

Q. keys

R. wax beans

S. corn pickers

T. gasoline

U. monuments

V. electric motors

W. rock wool

X. air conditioners

CONTRACTIONS: Sometimes two words are combined and shortened into one word by leaving out one or more letters. The shortened form is called a contraction. An apostrophe (') is used in the place of the letter or letters that are left out. Contractions are used more often in spoken language than in written language.

Make contractions for the following list of words.

Example: is not = isn't   I will = I'll

did not	1. _____	it is	11. _____
could not	2. _____	let us	12. _____
can not	3. _____	we have	13. _____
was not	4. _____	we shall	14. _____
had not	5. _____	were not	15. _____
would not	6. _____	you will	16. _____
has not	7. _____	we are	17. _____
I am	8. _____	there is	18. _____
I had	9. _____	they are	19. _____
do not	10. _____	she is	20. _____

QUESTIONS:

1. Why do people work? List six reasons.

    A. _____   D. _____

    B. _____   E. _____

    C. _____   F. _____

2. Why do people buy Government Savings Bonds?

3. Is work good or bad?   Why?

4. How can work make you feel important?

LESSON 3. INTEREST, APTITUDE, AND SKILL

There are many reasons why people choose one job over another. As students near the end of their school years, they begin to think about their job future. Young men and women must begin to think about what they would like to do and what they are able to do.

An interest is what one likes to do. It is a feeling of wanting to do or share in something. People might enjoy music, but they may not be able to play any musical instrument. We say they have an interest in music. A young person might like football, but is unable to play it. This is an interest.

An aptitude is some natural ability or talent a person has. If a young man or woman can do a job or learn to do it easily, it is said that they have an aptitude for the job. A person who knows how or can easily learn how to repair a car may have a mechanical aptitude. Anyone who can work with numbers quickly and accurately has a numerical ability or aptitude. Someone might have an interest in football, but may never become a Green Bay Packer because the necessary aptitude is lacking. In other words, the person may not be able to play well enough to be a professional football player, even though he has an interest in football. Young men or women may have an interest in nursing, but may not have the general learning ability or aptitude required to pass the classes necessary to become nurses. Of course, they could not become nurses, but they might

might become nurses' aides with the proper training.

Without an aptitude for a certain kind of work, one may not be able to develop an interest in the work. A young man who does not have the necessary manual dexterity may be unable to do mechanical work. A young man who does not have the manual dexterity necessary to repair an automobile may never develop an interest in automobile mechanics.

A skill is the ability to do a job on your own. It is the ability to do things well. Skill is the ability that is gained by practice and knowledge. The amount of skill that a person can develop depends upon the aptitude or the ability to develop the skill. It may also depend on the person's interest in the job. Without an interest in the job, one may never practice and train long enough to develop the skill. Bricklaying is a skill. It is developed by people who have the aptitude to do the work after months of training and practice.

A worker doing a simple job on an assembly line in a factory may not need the skill that the bricklayer needs. The factory job may require less time to learn, but it may also pay less.

It is important that students understand their aptitudes, interests, and skills before looking for employment. It is important that they know what they have to offer their employers. Everyone has interests, aptitudes, and skills. Some like to work indoors. Some like to work outdoors. Some like to work in old clothes. Others like to dress up for work. Do you know what your interests are?

Some people can work high in the air on building projects. Others would be afraid of working at great heights. Some people can work well with others as a salesperson would, while others work well with tools. Do you know what your aptitudes are?

Sometimes the only way to develop a skill is to find a job and work your way up to the goal you have set for yourself. For example, you may wish to become a carpenter working for a building firm. You might start out on the job carrying lumber for other carpenters. After a while, by moving up-the-ladder from one job to another, you finally become a carpenter. This is known as "on-the-job training".

A person might also develop some skill by attending a class or school. A person might develop a skill in welding by attending a vocational or technical school. Some employers and the military services may also provide training to develop skills.

WORDS: Use the dictionary to define the following words.

1.   manual:

2.   dexterity:

3.   accurate:

4.   mechanical:

5.   develop:

6.   practice:

7.   assembly line:

8.   scared:

9.   vocational:

10. ability:

BLANKS: Use the words below to fill in the blanks.

numerical   skill   aptitude   interest   mechanical

1.   Having an _____ for a job means being able to do a job or learning
     to do it easily.

2.   Having an _____ in a job means liking to do it.

3.   The ability to do a job well on your own is known as having a _____ .

4.   Working with numbers quickly and accurately is known as _____
     ability or aptitude.

5.   A person who works well with tools has a _____ aptitude.

TRUE or **FALSE**:   Place a "T" for true and an "F" for false before each statement.

_____   1.   An aptitude is what one likes to do.

_____   2.   A skill is the ability to do a job on your own.

_____   3.   Manual dexterity is necessary to be able to repair an automobile.

_____   4.   A skill is developed by training and practice.

_____   5.   General learning ability is not necessary to become a nurse.

_____   6.   Everyone has interests and aptitudes.

_____   7.   Everyone has the same aptitudes.

_____   8.   Talent means about the same thing as interest.

_____   9.   The military services provide training to develop some skills.

_____   10. Learning a skill while on the job is known as "on-the-job training".

INTERESTS: Place a checkmark next to the job interests you have.

		Interest	Examples
_____	1.	indoor work	factory worker - supermarket worker - restaurant worker
_____	2.	outdoor work	forester - vegetable picker - farmer - service station worker
_____	3.	working with people	nurses' aide - salesperson - foreman
_____	4.	helping people	doctor - nurse - teacher - priest
_____	5.	physical work	bricklayer - farmer - iron worker - road worker
_____	6.	working with machines	lathe operator - tractor operator - train engineer
_____	7.	mental work	lawyer - reporter - teacher - social worker
_____	8.	working with numbers	check-out clerk - accountant - service station worker
_____	9.	working with hands	auto-mechanic - assembly-line worker - painter
_____	10.	working with animals	pet shop worker - farmer - zoo worker

APTITUDES: Place a checkmark next to the job aptitudes you have.

Aptitude	Examples
_____ 1. understanding words and ideas; being able to use language well.	writer - secretary - teacher - author
_____ 2. ability to work with numbers.	cashier - check out at a store - bookkeeper - carpenter
_____ 3. ability to move fingers quickly and accurately.	typist - barber - beautician - surgeon
_____ 4. general learning ability (easy to learn new things).	teacher - lawyer - doctor - engineer - market researcher
_____ 5. ability to work with hands.	mechanic - stockgirl - nurses' aide
_____ 6. ability to move hands, feet, and body skillfully.	truck driver - carpenter - nurses' aide - service station worker - factory worker - orderly
_____ 7. ability to see mistakes.	secretary - clerk - reporter
_____ 8. ability to create new things.	architect - artist - florist - decorator
_____ 9. physical strength.	construction worker - farmer - shipping room worker
_____ 10. ability to act quickly.	assembly line worker - firefighter - police officer

MISSING LETTERS: Write in the missing letters of the words.

1. An in ___ ___ ___ est is what one likes to do.
2. An aptitude is some ta ___ ___ nt a person has.
3. A skill is the abi ___ ___ t ___ to do a job on your own.
4. An automobile mechanic needs manual de ___ te ___ ity.
5. Bricklaying is a ski ___ ___.
6. Students should understand their aptitudes, interests, and skills before looking for e ___ pl ___ ___ me ___ t.
7. Ever ___ on ___ has interests, aptitudes, and skills.
8. A person might develop some skill by at ___ en ___ ing a class or school.
9. Skill is the ability that is g ___ ined by practice and k ___ owl ___ dge.
10. It is imp ___ rtant that workers know what they have to of ___ ___ r to their employers.
11. Some people like to work ind ___ ___ rs. Some people like to work outdoors.
12. Do you know what your in ___ ere ___ t ___ are?

FANCY NAMES: In Column 2 is a fancy name for the job or occupation listed in Column 1. Match the fancy name with the common name.

Column 1

_____ 1.   maid

_____ 2.   cement finisher

_____ 3.   teacher

_____ 4.   housekeeper

_____ 5.   farmer

_____ 6.   automobile repairperson

_____ 7.   janitor

_____ 8.   cook's helper

_____ 9.   garbage collector

_____ 10. dry cleaning worker

_____ 11. babysitter

_____ 12. barber

_____ 13. tree planter

_____ 14. picture taker

Column 2

A. educator

B. kitchen aide

C. hair stylist

D. presser

E. mason

F. sanitation worker

G. agricultural worker

H. homemaker

I. mechanic

J. domestic worker

K. child care specialist

L. custodian

M. photographer

N. forester

SYNONYMS: Match the word from Column 1 that means the same or nearly the same as the word in Column 2.

Column 1

_____ 1.   enjoy

_____ 2.   end

_____ 3.   ability

_____ 4.   man

_____ 5.   job

_____ 6.   accurate

_____ 7.   manual

_____ 8.   simple

_____ 9.   scared

_____ 10. offer

_____ 11. woman

Column 2

A. talent

B. give

C. afraid

D. finish

E. correct

F. male

G. employment

H. like

I. easy

J. hands

K. female

FILING: Some jobs take place mostly indoors while other jobs are mostly outdoor jobs. Following is a list of indoor jobs and outdoor jobs. Put them in the correct column.

JOBS

A. nurses' aide

B. farmer

C. road construction worker

D. teacher

E. dishwasher

F. service station attendant

G. sales clerk

H. check-out clerk

I. bricklayer

J. truck driver

K. forester

L. TV repairperson

M. factory worker

N. domestic worker

O. carpenter's helper

P. bakery worker

Q. computer operator

R. gardener

S. sanitation worker

T. street cleaner

Indoor Jobs

1. _____
2. _____
3. _____
4. _____
5. _____
6. _____
7. _____
8. _____
9. _____
10. _____

Outdoor Jobs

1. _____
2. _____
3. _____
4. _____
5. _____
6. _____
7. _____
8. _____
9. _____
10. _____

QUESTIONS:

1. List three jobs in which you have an interest.

   A.

   B.

   C.

2. List three jobs for which you have an aptitude.

   A.

   B.

   C.

3. List three jobs for which you have the necessary skills.

   A.

   B.

   C.

4. Do you think you could play basketball for the Milwaukee Bucks? Why or why not?

LESSON 4. JOB SELECTION

Nearly one-half of the hours he/she is awake, the average working person will be on the job. Since so much time is spent working, it is important that the proper job be selected. One should be happy in the work that is chosen. Everyone should ask what is wanted from an occupation. A good job for one person may not be a good job another person. One person may enjoy cattle ranching because it is outdoor work, or because it is working with animals. Another may dislike this occupation. The work selected should be the right occupation for that person.

In this lesson, some factors that should be considered in job selection will be discussed. Most people would probably put the amount of wages or salary a job pays as the most important consideration in selecting employment. The things that most people can afford to buy will be determined by salary or wages received on the job. It is important to remember that the amount a person earns in one year is more important that what is made per hour or per day. For example, a construction worker might get a high hourly wage, but cannot work on rainy or cold winter days. The construction worker might make less per year than a person who would work all the working days of the year.

Overtime pay should also be considered. People generally receive a higher wage for that part of their work that exceeds forty hours per week. Overtime pay can make a big difference in the amount anyone earns per year.

Future salary or wage increases should also be kept in mind. Most good jobs will pay more after the worker has been on the job for six months or a year. It is important not only to see how much a job pays now, but also how much it will pay in the future. A young person may need more money five years from now that he/she needs at the present time. In five years, there may be a family who must be supported.

Where the job is located is also an important consideration in selecting an occupation. If employment is near one's home, there will be less cost in getting to work. Many jobs are found in large cities while other jobs are in small towns or on farms. Many large city jobs pay more than jobs in small towns, but the cost of living is also higher in the large city. Where to live is an important consideration before looking for work.

Some people work during the day, while others work the evening shift, and still others might work during the night. Most people work from Monday through Friday, but others must work on weekends or holidays. The hours one has to work are an important consideration in selecting employment.

Whether a job meets the interests, aptitudes, and skills of the worker is also important. The best kind of job would be work that a person could enjoy. If this is not possible, at least a worker should not hate the job. Anyone who has trouble getting along with others would probably make a poor nurses' aide. Someone who is not handy with tools may make a poor auto-mechanic. Taking a job that is not suited to personal interests, aptitudes, or skills may result in getting fired or released from the job at a later date.

Some job positions are seasonal. This means the employer hires workers only for a certain season or seasons of the year. For example, a bean canning company may hire workers only during the late summer canning season. Some jobs are part-time. This means the employee works less than forty hours per week. For example, a restaurant may hire a dishwasher for only two hours each evening.

Some full-time occupations do not offer much job security. Some employers hire workers during their busy seasons and then lay these employees off during their slow business periods. Generally, the first worker to be laid-off from a job is the one who was hired last. Is the job permanent? Does it offer steady work? These are important considerations in job selection.

Another important factor in job selection is the kind of employee benefits that are given by the employer. These benefits include such things as time-off, discounts, sick pay, retirement payments, bonuses for good work, and health and life insurance payments. These employee benefits are known as "fringe benefits" and will be discussed in a later lesson.

Before selecting employment, a worker should also consider the type of working conditions that the job offers. Some jobs are located in clean, pleasant surroundings, while others are located in noisy, dirty surroundings. Some jobs offer safety to the worker while others are quite dangerous. Some work is indoors; some work is outdoors. The person selecting a job must find desirable working conditions or be able to adjust to the working conditions of the job.

Whether the work offers advancement is another important consideration in job selection. Some jobs allow a worker to move "up-the-ladder" with an improved salary, while other work does not offer much chance for advancement. Many companies provide on-the-job training so that the employee may get a promotion on the job. The person looking for a job should set goals for the future. It may be more important to know what the work will provide five, ten, or even twenty years from now than what it provides today. The worker should ask himself whether the job can be done by a machine in the near or distant future. If it can be done by machine, he might be out of a job at some time in the future.

Selecting a job is one of the most important decisions made during a lifetime. It should be studied and not be a hit-or-miss decision.

MATCHING: Match the words in Column 1 with the correct meaning in Column 2.

Column 1   Column 2

_____   1. proper   A. coming; time to come

_____   2. occupation   B. employment; person's work

_____   3. select   C. lasting; not for a short time

_____   4. wages   D. let go; let loose

_____   5. salary   E. advance or getting ahead in rank or
                                                               importance

_____   6. future   F. amount paid for work; paid by hour or day

_____   7. consideration   G. thinking about things in order to decide them

_____   8. released   H. correct; right

_____   9. permanent   I. fixed pay for work; paid by month or year

_____ 10. promotion   J. picked as best; choose

ANTONYMS: Match the word of Column 1 with the opposite meaning word in Column 2.

Example: love - hate

Column 1   Column 2

_____   1. spend   A. same

_____   2. different   B. indoor

_____   3. pleasant   C. receives

_____   4. dislike   D. temporary

_____   5. outdoor   E. disagreeable

_____   6. employed   F. demotion

_____   7. promotion   G. unemployed

_____   8. permanent   H. fire

_____   9. future   I. save

_____ 10. evening   J. like

_____ 11. hire   K. morning

_____ 12. gives   L. past

_____ 13. awake   M. decrease

_____ 14. handy   N. unskilled

_____ 15. increase   O. asleep

_____ 16. dangerous   P. farm

_____ 17. city   Q. clumsy

_____ 18. skilled   R. safe

TRUE or FALSE: Place a "T" for true and an "F" for false before each statement.

_____ 1. The work selected should be the correct job for that person.

_____ 2. Benefits such as sick pay, insurance payments, and retirement payments are called fringe benefits.

_____ 3. Many companies provide on-the-job training for their employees.

_____ 4. Salary is an important factor to consider when looking at a job.

_____ 5. All people enjoy the same kind of work.

_____ 6. A good job should offer some chance for advancement in the future.

_____ 7. Selecting a job should be a hit-or-miss decision.

_____ 8. Overtime pay is always paid at the same rate as regular pay.

_____ 9. Generally, the first worker to be laid off from a job is the one who was hired last.

_____ 10. Overtime pay can make a big difference in the amount of pay a worker earns per year.

ROOT WORDS: Place the root words found in the following words on the blank spaces.

Example: working (work)   nearly (near)

1. selected _____   8. located _____

2. personal _____   9. seasonal _____

3. considered _____   10. employer _____

4. employment _____   11. surrounding _____

5. hourly _____   12. consideration _____

6. worker _____   13. selecting _____

7. received _____   14. safety _____

SPELLING WORDS: Correct the following misspelled words.

1. importent _____   7. possable _____

2. occupaton _____   8. seazonal _____

3. caning _____   9. troubl _____

4. remenber _____   10. restarant _____

5. durning _____   11. pleasent _____

6. suport _____   12. decesion _____

JOB CLASSIFICATION: From the following list of jobs, place each job in one of the four groups below:

1.	garage handyperson	13.	pot washer
2.	vegetable seller	14.	mechanic's helper
3.	greenhouse attendant	15.	car washer
4.	sod farm laborer	16.	gardener
5.	parking lot attendant	17.	dyer
6.	presser	18.	waiter
7.	steward	19.	starcher
8.	tagger	20.	egg handler
9.	florist's helper	21.	fruit picker
10.	gasoline station attendant	22.	waitress
11.	dryer	23.	steam table serviceperson
12.	spotter	24.	chauffeur

Food Preparation and Service

1. _____

2. _____

3. _____

4. _____

5. _____

6. _____

Motor Vehicle Operation & Service

1. _____

2. _____

3. _____

4. _____

5. _____

6. _____

Laundering, Cleaning, & Dyeing

1. _____

2. _____

3. _____

4. _____

5. _____

6. _____

Agriculture

1. _____

2. _____

3. _____

4. _____

5. _____

6. _____

MISSING LETTERS: Write in the missing letters of the words.

1.   Everyone should ask what is wanted from an occ ___ p ___ tion.

2.   One should be ha ___ py in the work that is ch ___ sen.

3.   Where to live is an important con ___ ider ___ tion before I ___ ___ king for work.

4.   The hours one has to work are an imp ___ ___ tant consideration in sel ___ ___ ting employment.

5.   Some job p ___ ___ itions are seasonal.

6.   Many companies pro ___ ide on-the-job train ___ ___ g for employees.

7.   The person looking at a job should set his/her g ___ als for the f ___ ___ ure.

8.   Sele ___ ___ ing a job is one of the most important decisions made during a I ___ fe ___ ime.

HOMONYMS: Some words sound alike but have different meanings and are spelled differently. These words are called homonyms. Write one homonym for each of the words listed below: (Check your spelling in the dictionary.)

Example: right - <u>write</u>   blew - <u>blue</u>

1. aunt	_____	6. coarse	_____	11. sea	_____
2. flour	_____	7. their	_____	12. dye	_____
3. weak	_____	8. pear	_____	13. new	_____
4. bare	_____	9. wring	_____	14. be	_____
5. do	_____	10. prays	_____	15. two	_____

QUESTIONS:

1.   What factors should be considered before selecting a job? List below.

A. _____   E. _____

B. _____   F. _____

C. _____   G. _____

D. _____   H. _____

(continued)

2.   What is overtime pay?

3.   What kind of job would you like to have during your lifetime? Give reasons for your answer.

4.   Why is the location of a job important to the worker?

5.   What is seasonal work?

6.   What is meant by working conditions on the job?

7.   What does it mean to be promoted on the job?

LESSON 5. LOCATING EMPLOYERS

After interests, aptitudes, and skills of the worker are determined, he/she must find an employer who wants to hire someone with these talents. It is necessary to find an employer who is looking for someone to fill a job opening in a company. Even after an opening is found, there is no guarantee that a person will be hired. It is best if anyone looking for work has several employers in mind. The worker has a better chance of getting a job if there are several employers on the "help wanted" list.

Knowing where to look for work is very important. When people do not know where to find work, they may not find a job that they want or an employer who can use their aptitudes and skills.

There are many good ways to find a job. Some of them will be discussed in this lesson. Probably the method that most young men and women use to find a job is asking friends and relatives. Sometimes friends and relatives hear about job openings at the places they work. They may also know or hear about other companies that are hiring new workers. Many times jobs are posted on bulletin boards in factories. The people working in the factory know about these jobs long before they are placed in the want-ads. Want-ads are advertisements in the newspaper that list job openings.

Another way to find a job is to do some "leg-work." After determining what kind of a job he/she wants, the job hunter goes from employer to employer and files an application for work. This method takes time, but many times it pays off. In many small towns and cities, jobs are often filled this way. The job is filled before it has a chance to be advertised. This is often true of the good jobs because people want them. After an application for a job is made with an employer, go back once a month or so to show your interest in employment.

Checking the want-ads in the newspaper is also a good way to find work. Many large companies, as well as many small ones, use the newspaper want-ads to fill job vacancies. If the want-ad is used as a method for finding employment, the directions given in the want-ad should be followed closely. If the directions give a telephone number to call for an appointment, be sure to call rather than go directly to the company. Employers feel that people who do not follow directions make poor employees.

Available jobs can also be found by searching the Internet. There are many websites available that list job openings nationwide.

State Employment Offices are found in most large cities as well as many smaller cities to help people find work. Sometimes these offices are called "Job Service offices." These offices not only have lists of job openings, but also assist job hunters in other ways. Tests may be provided that help to secure employment. The tests generally will give information on interests and aptitude. The State Employment Office also gives advice to the job hunter. This advice is called "counseling." Counseling helps the job hunter find out what jobs are best suited for the young worker. All services of the State Employment Offices are free.

Private employment groups may also give assistance in finding employment. The names of these groups can be found in the newspaper want-ads or the telephone Yellow Pages. The private employment groups give the same kind of help as the State Employment Offices. It should be remembered that the private employment groups charge for their help. Either the employee or the employer or both the employee and the employer will pay if employment is secured. Before any papers are signed with a private employment group, it is wise for the job seeker to know what is being signed. Usually a part of the worker's earnings will go to the private employment group to help pay for this service.

The Yellow Pages of the telephone book are helpful in finding the names of possible employers. The Yellow Pages do not list any jobs that are vacant, but will list companies or employers by the type of work or business they do. If one is looking for work as a plumber's helper, the Yellow Pages will list all the plumbers in the city. From this point on, "leg-work" by the job seeker may be required.

Federal Post Office job announcements may be found posted in the Post Office. State Civil Service jobs are generally posted in state buildings. The announcement gives the description of the job, the qualifications necessary for the job, the pay, as well as how and where to apply. Civil Service jobs are filled after a written test and an interview.

Job vacancies might also be posted on bulletin boards at local churches, Y.M.C.A.'s, Y.W.C.A.'s, community centers, or other neighborhood groups. If the jobs are not listed, people at these organizations may know of work available in the surrounding area.

Another way to find a job is to talk to a high school counselor or a teacher. Many high school counselors and some teachers keep a file of jobs that are open. These people may be able to test for interests and aptitudes as well as offer advice on job hunting.

It is important that a person looking for work try as many methods as possible to find it. Looking for work is not always easy. There may be times when the applicant may think that a job will never be found. He or she must not give up, however, but must continue to look. The person who waits for the job to come to him/her may stay unemployed.

MATCHING: Match the words in Column 1 with the correct meaning in Column 2.

Column 1		Column 2
_____	1. unemployed	A. make public; put up in a place to be seen
_____	2. vacancy	B. promise; pledge; stand back of
_____	3. guarantee	C. give public notice; announce
_____	4. method	D. giving advice to someone
_____	5. posted	E. way of doing something
_____	6. application	F. people out of work
_____	7. advertise	G. work; what a person is doing
_____	8. appointment	H. opening; unoccupied job
_____	9. counseling	I. request; applying for work
_____	10. employment	J. set a time or place to be somewhere or meet someone

MULTIPLE CHOICE: Select the one best answer.

_____ 1. To find job openings in a newspaper a person would look at the -

     A.   society page
     B.   want-ads
     C.   front page

_____ 2. The charge for finding a job through a State Employement Office is -

     A.   one week's pay
     B.   nothing
     C.   a percentage of the first month's pay

_____ 3. To find the names of all the plumbers in a city, a person would look at -

     A.   want-ads
     B.   Yellow Pages
     C.   TV advertisements

_____ 4. Civil Service jobs are -

     A.   government jobs
     B.   big business jobs
     C.   mechanical jobs

_____ 5. A person can find a private employment group by looking -

     A.   in the want-ads
     B.   in the Yellow Pages
     C.   in either of these

SPELLING WORDS: Correct the misspelled words.

1. imployer   _____

2. skils   _____

3. compamy   _____

4. bullentin   _____

5. discused   _____

6. methed   _____

7. aplication   _____

8. employar   _____

9. counsling   _____

10. telaphone   _____

SYLLABLES: Use a dictionary to divide the words into syllables.

1. vacancy   _____

2. aptitude   _____

3. probably   _____

4. job   _____

5. determine   _____

6. newspaper   _____

7. guarantee   _____

8. description   _____

9. generally   _____

10. advertise   _____

TRUE or FALSE: Place a "T" for true and an "F" for false before each statement.

_____   1.   Knowing where to look for work is important.

_____   2.   If a person applies for a job, he/she is guaranteed the job.

_____   3.   The Yellow Pages contain a list of present job openings.

_____   4.   Private employment services are free.

_____   5.   State Employment Offices sometimes give tests to job hunters.

_____   6.   After an application for a job is made it is not a good idea to check back with the employer.

_____   7.   Civil Service job announcements give a description of the job.

_____   8.   Many young people find jobs through their friends or relatives.

_____   9.   The want-ads in a newspaper are a poor way of finding work.

_____   10.   All job openings are advertised in the newspaper.

_____   11.   Civil Service jobs are filled after a written test and an interview.

_____   12.   High school counselors may give interest and aptitude tests.

ALPHABETICAL ORDER: Put the list of jobs below in alphabetical (ABC) order.

domestic worker   1. _____

plumber's helper   2. _____

carpenter   3. _____

dishwasher   4. _____

factory worker   5. _____

assembly-line worker   6. _____

orderly   7. _____

florist   8. _____

cook   9. _____

housekeeper   10. _____

nurses' aide   11. _____

janitor   12. _____

MANUAL WORKERS: Anyone who works chiefly with their hands is called a manual worker. Sometimes these people are called "blue-collar" workers. The name probably comes from the fact that many of these workers wear blue work shirts. Manual or blue-collar workers transport all kinds of materials in the country. The people who manufacture things in factories are blue-collar workers.

Following is a list of occupations. Place the letter "M" before all those that are manual.

_____ 1. mason	_____ 7. truck driver	_____ 13. sheet-metal worker
_____ 2. teacher	_____ 8. minister	_____ 14. TV announcer
_____ 3. doctor	_____ 9. salesperson	_____ 15. assembly-line worker
_____ 4. welder	_____ 10. road worker	_____ 16. machine operator
_____ 5. pipefitter	_____ 11. nurse	_____ 17. TV repairperson
_____ 6. electrician	_____ 12. bakery worker	_____ 18. auto-mechanic

ABBREVIATIONS: An abbreviation is a short way of writing a word. In many newspaper want-ads and work places, abbreviations are used to save space. Using the two groups shown below, match the abbreviation with the word or words for which it stands.

(See examples - "secretary" and "temporary")

A.	including	O.	hour	CC.	references
B.	heavy	P.	graduate	DD.	part-time
C.	year	Q.	good	EE.	prefer
D.	week	R.	future	FF.	junior
E.	month	S.	department	GG.	manufacture
F.	manager	T.	company	HH.	necessary
G.	paid	U.	corporation	II.	experience
H.	afternoon	V.	headquarters	JJ.	and so forth
I.	employment	W.	worker	KK.	excellent
J.	equipment	X.	trainee	LL.	building
K.	advertising	Y.	secretary	MM.	appointment
L.	morning	Z.	temporary	NN.	beginning
M.	business	AA.	mechanical	OO.	license
N.	high school	BB.	salary	PP.	senior

__Y__ a. secy.   __Z__ aa. temp.

_____	1. appt.	_____	15. nec.	_____	28. hqtrs.
_____	2. bgn.	_____	16. P.M.	_____	29. sr.
_____	3. bldg.	_____	17. A.M.	_____	30. mgr.
_____	4. hr.	_____	18. exp.	_____	31. pd.
_____	5. H.S.	_____	19. gd.	_____	32. lic.
_____	6. incl.	_____	20. grad.	_____	33. jr.
_____	7. dept.	_____	21. corp.	_____	34. eqpt.
_____	8. wk.	_____	22. trnee.	_____	35. pt.
_____	9. yr.	_____	23. wkr.	_____	36. etc.
_____	10. sal.	_____	24. mo.	_____	37. exc.
_____	11. refs.	_____	25. empl.	_____	38. bus.
_____	12. pref.	_____	26. co.	_____	39. hvy.
_____	13. manuf.	_____	27. adv.	_____	40. ftr.
_____	14. mech.				

FILING: Some jobs require mostly physical work (lifting - carrying - walking - etc.) while other jobs require mostly mental work (thinking). Following is a list of physical and mental jobs. Put them in the correct column.

Jobs

1. hammersmith
2. meter reader
3. interpreter
4. road worker
5. busboy
6. riding stable helper
7. custodian's helper
8. air traffic controller
9. bank teller
10. vocational counselor

11. fruit picker
12. rabbi
13. salesperson
14. telephone operator
15. postal clerk
16. dishwasher
17. garbage collector
18. assembler
19. librarian
20. iron worker

Physical Jobs

1. _____
2. _____
3. _____
4. _____
5. _____
6. _____
7. _____
8. _____
9. _____
10. _____

Mental Jobs

1. _____
2. _____
3. _____
4. _____
5. _____
6. _____
7. _____
8. _____
9. _____
10. _____

JOB CLASSIFICATION: Following is a list of jobs. Place each job under the type of work it is.

1.   janitor
2.   machine shop helper
3.   asphalt placer
4.   elevator operator
5.   garbage collector
6.   child care worker
7.   sorter of manufacturing supplies
8.   housekeeper
9.   window cleaner
10. cook's helper
11. tree trimmer
12. handyperson

13. foundry worker
14. attendant for semi-invalid
15. laundress
16. packager of supplies
17. painter
18. door attendant
19. lathe operator
20. machine tool operator
21. floor scrubber
22. truck driver
23. leaf raker
24. sewer repairer

Building Maintenance and Operation

1. _____
2. _____
3. _____
4. _____
5. _____
6. _____

General Factory Work

1. _____
2. _____
3. _____
4. _____
5. _____
6. _____

City Streets and Sanitation

1. _____
2. _____
3. _____
4. _____
5. _____
6. _____

Domestic Service

1. _____
2. _____
3. _____
4. _____
5. _____
6. _____

PROBLEMS AND QUESTIONS:

1. List eight places a person might find information on job openings.

    A. _____   E. _____

    B. _____   F. _____

    C. _____   G. _____

    D. _____   H. _____

2. What is "leg-work" in job hunting?

3. List two places a person might receive advice on job aptitudes and interests.

    A. _____

    B. _____

4. Why should anyone go out and look for a job?

5. How would a person find the State Employment office?

6. How do State Employment offices and Private Employment Offices differ?

7. How may friends and relatives help a person find a job?

LESSON 6. LETTER OF APPLICATION

There are generally four ways of contacting an employer about a job. They are the following:

1. Using the telephone.
2. Going directly to the personnel office.
3. Writing a letter of application.
4. Using the Internet.

After finding a desirable job opening, the applicant must decide on the best method to use in contacting the employer. If the employer gives a telephone number in the want-ad, the telephone should be used as the first contact. Some employers do not want to be troubled with telephone calls. In this case, the applicant should go in person or write a letter. Sometimes it is difficult to arrange a personal interview with an employer without some earlier contact. If this is the case, then a letter of application should be written. Many employers prefer letters of application and some employers even require them.

A letter of application gives much information about the person writing the letter. Employers not only get the information written in the letter, but they also see how well the letter is written. It serves as a good record for the future.

A poor letter of application can close the "job door" for a person. If it is written poorly or incorrectly, the employer may never contact the person about the job. However, a well-written letter may be the applicant's best chance of getting the job that is desired.

It should be remembered that the purpose of the letter of application is to get an interview with the employer. It is only the first step in getting a job, but it is an important step. If the letter does not meet the employer's approval, the writer will get no further in the job hunt.

A letter of application is a business letter. Like all business letters, it has six main parts. The parts and an explanation of each part follow:

1. <u>Heading</u>

The heading of a letter should be written along the top left margin of the page. It should give the writer's address and the date the letter was written.

<u>Example</u>:   705 Main Street
Merrill, Wisconsin 54452
January 24, _____

2. <u>Inside Address</u>

The inside address of a letter should be written on the left margin of the page. It should give the name, position, and address of the person to whom the letter is being sent.

<u>Example</u>:   Ms. Ann Ricci
Director of Personnel
Acme Manufacturing Corporation
1164 Second Street
Merrill, Wisconsin 54452

3. <u>Greeting</u>

The greeting of the letter should be written on the left margin below the inside address. It is the way of addressing the one to whom the letter is being sent. If the letter is being sent to a particular person, the last name may be used in the greeting. If the letter is to a company where the name of the person is not known, it may be addressed "Dear Sir."

<u>Examples</u>:   Dear Sir: -Dear Mr. Ricci: -Dear Ms. Bronski:

4. <u>Body</u>

The body of a letter tells what one person wants to say to another. It is the most important part of the letter. The body of the letter should tell the purpose of the letter. It should tell the employer the job for which that person is applying. The body should also give some information on the applicant's education and training.

A short history of past work experience should be included in the body. This gives the employer some idea of the applicant's skills and knowledge of the job. It is also a good idea to include one or two references in the body of the letter. These references should know the applicant well. If possible, one of the references should be the boss or supervisor on the applicant's last job.

5. Closing Phrase

The closing phrase of a letter should be written along the left margin of the page following the body.

Example: Sincerely,   Sincerely yours,   Yours truly,

6. Signature

The signature is the name of the person writing the letter. It should be below the closing phrase. It is never typed or printed.

A good letter of application should be typed or written with blue or black ink. It should be neat and only as long as necessary to give the important information. It should be written on only one side of unlined paper.

A. Sample Envelope

```
Mr. John Engler
705 Main Street
Merrill, Wisconsin  54452




                                Ms. Ann Ricci
                                Director of Personnel
                                Acme Manufacturing Corporation
                                1164 Second Street
                                Merrill, Wisconsin  54452
```

B. Sample letter of application. Notice the proper form, correct capitalization, and proper punctuation in the letter on the following page.

705 Main Street
Merrill, Wisconsin   54452
January 24, _____

Ms. Ann Ricci
Director of Personnel
Acme Manufacturing Corporation
1164 Second Street
Merrill, Wisconsin   54452

Dear Ms. Ricci:

I am writing to you to apply for the job as janitor that was
advertised in the Merrill Daily Herald.

I am nineteen years old and a graduate of Merrill High School,
Merrill, Wisconsin. During the time I attended high school,
I worked as a janitor's helper as part of a work-study program.

During the past year, I have been working full-time as a
janitor's helper at the Lincoln County Courthouse, 608 North Avenue,
Merrill, Wisconsin. My boss, Mr. Donald Schmidt, has indicated
that I could use him as a reference.

I will be happy to furnish you with any more information
that you may desire. I feel that I can do a good job for you as a janitor
in your company. I would appreciate the opportunity of a personal
interview. If you wish to call, my telephone number is 555-5711.

Sincerely yours,

John Engler

John Engler

MATCHING: Match the words in Column 1 with the correct meaning in Column 2.

Column 1

_____ 1. contacting

_____ 2. personnel office

_____ 3. applicant

_____ 4. troubled

_____ 5. personal

_____ 6. interview

_____ 7. approval

_____ 8. explanation

_____ 9. margin

_____ 10. knowledge

_____ 11. unlined

_____ 12. capitalization

_____ 13. punctuation

_____ 14. reference

_____ 15. appreciate

Column 2

A. tell the meaning of something; make clear;
   tell how to do something

B. a person who applies for a job

C. fact of knowing; that which is learned

D. to meet with someone about a job

E. writing or printing with capital letters

F. cause extra work; disturbed; bothered

G. be thankful for a favor or help

H. consent; being in favor of something

I. get in touch with someone

J. using periods, commas, and other marks
   to help make the meaning clear

K. done in person; directly to oneself

L. space around a page that has no
   writing or printing on it

M. having no lines

N. a person who will speak well of another
   person applying for a job

O. place where a person goes to apply
   for a job

TRUE or FALSE: Place a "T" for true and an "F" for false before each statement.

_____ 1. The letter of application should be written with a sharp pencil.

_____ 2. Red ink is a good color to use when writing a letter of application.

_____ 3. Some employers require a letter of application.

_____ 4. When writing a letter of application, both sides of the paper should
           be used so there is not any waste.

_____ 5. The letter of application should be written on lined paper.

_____ 6. The "signature" is printed neatly.

_____ 7. The letter of application contains five main parts.

(continued)

_____ 8. In the "closing", only the first word is capitalized.

_____ 9. The "body" of the letter is not a very important part.

_____ 10. The "inside address" gives the address of the sender of the letter.

_____ 11. Proper punctuation is important in a business letter.

_____ 12. A letter of application is a business letter.

_____ 13. The main purpose of the letter of application is to get an interview with the employer.

_____ 14. The "heading" of the letter is placed in the upper right hand corner of the page.

_____ 15. The date the letter is written is put in the "inside address."

_____ 16. The "inside address" is written on the left margin of the page.

_____ 17. A colon may be placed after the "greeting" of the business letter.

_____ 18. A good letter of application should never be typed.

_____ 19. A short history of the applicant's past work experience should be included in the "body" of the letter.

_____ 20. The "heading" gives the address of the sender of the letter.

MULTIPLE CHOICE: Select the one best answer.

_____ 1. The name of at least one reference should be found in the

    A. heading   B. inside address   C. body

_____ 2. The person to whom the business letter is being sent is found in the

    A. heading   B. inside address   C. body

_____ 3. Information on the applicant's training and education should appear in the

    A. heading   B. inside address   C. body

_____ 4. The "greeting" of the letter should be written on the left margin below the

    A. heading   B. inside address   C. body

_____ 5. The business letter has

    A. three main parts   B. five main parts   C. six main parts

JOB CLASSIFICATION: Following is a list of jobs. Place each job under the kind of work it is.

1. furniture store worker

2. furniture factory worker

3. cheese maker

4. appliance store worker

5. room cleaner

6. valet services

7. poultry dressing worker

8. paint store worker

9. janitor

10. candy factory worker

11. maple sugar forest worker

12. reforestation worker

13. saw mill worker

14. hardware store worker

15. butcher

16. steam table helper

17. Christmas tree farm worker

18. dishwasher

19. clothing store worker

20. department store worker

21. vegetable cannery worker

22. waitress

23. box factory worker

24. frozen foods packer

Sales Work

1. _____

2. _____

3. _____

4. _____

5. _____

6. _____

Forestry and Lumber Work

1. _____

2. _____

3. _____

4. _____

5. _____

6. _____

Food Products Work

1. _____

2. _____

3. _____

4. _____

5. _____

6. _____

Restaurant - Hotel Work

1. _____

2. _____

3. _____

4. _____

5. _____

6. _____

MATCHING OCCUPATIONS: Listed below are some job titles and what workers do on the job. Match the job with the work.

_____ 1. maid

A. repair books, move books, sort books and papers

_____ 2. stock person

B. mark merchandise, package merchandise, stock shelves, and clean store

_____ 3. meat market helper

C. pick-up and deliver mail, run errands, distribute materials

_____ 4. pet shop helper

D. wash and iron clothes

_____ 5. library assistant

E. carry trays, clear dishes from table, set tables, mop floors

_____ 6. general office messenger

F. make beds, wash windows, care for children, sweep

_____ 7. laundry worker

G. handle meat products, cut meat, package meat, clean store

_____ 8. cook's helper

H. care for and clean animals

_____ 9. restaurant dining room helper

I. prepare and cook foods, mop floors, make sandwiches

_____ 10. dishwasher

J. drive tractor, bale hay, feed and care for animals

_____ 11. carpenter's helper

K. scrape dishes, wash and dry dishes, polish silver

_____ 12. delivery person

L. pump gas, wash cars, clear snow, wash windshields

_____ 13. truck driver

M. run errands, deliver goods or supplies to customers, wrap packages

_____ 14. service station attendant

N. drive truck, haul goods and supplies

_____ 15. farm laborer

O. drive nails, measure lumber, saw boards, putty holes, carry lumber

SINGULAR/PLURAL:

When a word means only one, it is singular. When it means more than one, it is plural. Most words are changed from singular to plural by adding the letter "s". Words that end in "x", "s", "sh", or "ch" are changed from singular to plural by adding "es". Add either "s" or "es" to make the following list of words plural.

Example: employer - employers   box - boxes

1. way   _____   3. class   _____

2. job   _____   4. method   _____

(continued)

SINGULAR/PLURAL, continued

5. person _____   18. letter _____

6. record _____   19. skill _____

7. glass _____   20. dress _____

8. door _____   21. dish _____

9. dash _____   22. interview _____

10. part _____   23. phrase _____

11. six _____   24. signature _____

12. page _____   25. lunch _____

13. address _____   26. print _____

14. margin _____   27. paper _____

15. name _____   28. side _____

16. brush _____   29. church _____

17. helper _____   30. applicant _____

ACTIVITIES:

1. On a separate piece of paper, write a letter of application to Mr. Roy Vanguard,
    Ace Plumbers, 1406 East Third Street, Your Town, Your State, applying for the
    job of plumber's helper. Write the letter just as if you were applying for the job. Check
    back in the lesson to be sure you use all the proper rules for a good letter of application.

2. On a separate piece of paper, make a 3 1/2" x 6 1/2" outline of an envelope.
    Address the envelope with the information given in Activity 1.

SENTENCE ORDER: Number the following sentences in the order in which they
                        appeared in this lesson. The first sentence is done for you.

_____ A short history of the applicant's past work experience should be included in the body.

_____ The signature is the name of the person writing the letter.

__1__ There are generally four ways of contacting an employer about a job.

_____ Many employers prefer letters of application and some employers even
         require them.

_____ A good letter of application should be typed or written with black or blue ink.

(continued)

SENTENCE ORDER, continued

_____ The closing phrase should be written on the left hand side of the letter following the body.

_____ It is also a good idea to include one or two references in the body of the letter.

_____ A letter of application is a business letter.

_____ It is the way of addressing a person to whom the letter is being sent.

_____ A poor letter of application can close the "job door" for a person.

ALPHABETICAL ORDER: Put the list of jobs that follow in alphabetical (ABC) order.

road maintenance worker   1. _____

grounds keeper   2. _____

assembly line worker   3. _____

car wash worker   4. _____

building construction worker   5. _____

forestry worker   6. _____

janitor   7. _____

nurses' aide   8. _____

cannery worker   9. _____

seamstress   10. _____

plumber's helper   11. _____

highway construction worker   12. _____

garbage collector   13. _____

painter's helper   14. _____

beauty shop helper   15. _____

QUESTIONS:

1. What is the purpose of a letter of application?

2. When should a letter of application be written?

(continued)

3. List the six main parts of a letter of application.

    A. _____

    B. _____

    C. _____

    D. _____

    E. _____

    F. _____

4. List three types of information that should be included in the "body" of a letter of application.

    A. _____

    B. _____

    C. _____

5. List four ways you could contact an employer about a job.

    A. _____

    B. _____

    C. _____

    D. _____

6. List two reasons why some employers require a letter of application.

    A. _____

    B. _____

LETTER ERRORS: Following is a letter of application that contains mistakes in spelling, capitalization, punctuation, letters left out, and letters in the wrong order. Circle each of the mistakes. The correct form of this letter can be found earlier in this lesson. Check back in the lesson if you need help. (There are thirty-five mistakes.)

---

705 main Street
Merrill Wisconsin 54452
January 24, _____

Ms Ann Ricci
Director of Personel
Acme Manufacturng corporation
1164 Second street
Merrill, Wisconsin 54452

Dear ms. Rici.

I am writing to you to aply for the job as janator that was advertised in the <u>Merrill</u> <u>daily</u> <u>Herald</u>.

I am ninteen years old and a garduate of Merrill high School Merrill Wisconsin
During the time I attended high School I worked as a janitors helper as a part of a
work-study program.

During the past year i have been working full time as a janitor's helper at the
lincoln county Courthouse, 608 north Avenue, Merrill Wisconsin. My boss Mr Donald
Schmidt, has indicated that I could use him as a reference.

I will be happy to furnish you with anymore information that you may desire.
I feel that I can do a job for you as a janitor in you compay. I would appreciate the
opportunity of a personal interveiw. If you wish to call, my telephone number is 555-5711

Sincerely Yours

John Engler

John Engler

LESSON 7. JOB APPLICATION FORMS.

In the last lesson, we learned that after locating a job one would like, the next step is to contact the employer. This contact might be made by telephone, letter of application, or going directly to the personnel office of the place the person wishes to work. When picking up an application it is important to appear neat and clean. If the employer feels that that person might fit the job, the applicant is asked to fill out an employment application. Nearly everyone who applies for a job must fill out an application.

It is important to use careful thought and planning when filling out the employment application. How well an application is filled out may mean the difference between getting or not getting the job. If the job application is filled out incorrectly, the applicant may never be called in for an interview.

Application forms differ from one company to another, but all of them ask for most of the same facts. If these facts are known, there should be no trouble filling out the forms. Someone looking for a job should get a small notebook where all the necessary facts can be kept. This will make it possible to fill out the application faster and to list the information correctly.

When filling out the application, it is important to be neat. Before considering an applicant for the job, the employer judges the type of person an applicant is by how he/she appears and the neatness of the application. Most employers do not care for sloppy workers. An untidy applicant or application may mean a sloppy person.

Employers also like workers who can follow directions. Employers judge how well people follow direction by the way they fill out their applications. If the form says print, it should not be written. If it calls for the last name first, the first name should not be printed first. The employer may also watch for mistakes made on the form. Mistakes on an application may be a reason for not hiring an individual. It is important to get everything in the correct places.

The employment application should be filled out completely. None of the parts should be missed. Missing parts of the form may show carelessness or lack of information necessary to fill out the form correctly. This may be another reason for not getting hired. If a question is not answered by the applicant, the word none should be written in or a line drawn in the blank space. The employer then knows that it was not just overlooked.

The following is a list of information anyone should have in a notebook before trying to fill out an application form. Some of the information may not be needed when the application is filed, but may be needed after the person gets the job. At that time, the worker may need to fill out additional forms. All information should be spelled correctly.

1. Parent's or guardian's name, home address, and home phone number. This should include the mother's maiden name.

2. Parent's or guardian's work address and phone number at work. This should include the name of the company.

3. A list of places or employers where the applicant has worked before. This should include the name of the company, the company address, the name of the boss or supervisor, the phone number, the starting date, and the last date of employment.

4. The applicant's permanent address, temporary address, and phone numbers. A temporary address is an address where a person is living if not living at the place called home. The permanent address is where someone will know where to find the applicant. It is where mail can be delivered.

5. The name, address, and phone number of a person to be called in case of an emergency.

6. The names and addresses of schools attended. This should also show the dates of attendance at school.

7. The names, addresses, and phone numbers of three or four references. The references should be an adult who knows the applicant quite well and is willing to answer questions the employer might have about him or her. References should not be relatives. It may also be wise to include the occupations and job titles of the references.

8. A list of clubs or organizations to which the applicant belongs. This should include any office held.

9. Social Security Number.

10. A list of the sports, hobbies, and activities in which the person has an interest.

Most employment applications will ask the amount of salary or pay that is expected. It is probably best to answer "going rate" or "open". "Going rate" means whatever the employer is paying for the job. "Open" means that the salary or wage can be discussed during the time of the interview. Putting down too large a pay figure may keep the person from getting the job. Putting down too small a pay figure may keep the person from possibly getting a higher salary or wage.

Remember that when people fill out application forms, they are trying to sell themselves to the employer. They are trying to convince the employer that they are the best for the job. This can only be done by being neat and correct.

Study the filled out application form on the next page.

ACME MANUFACTURING COMPANY
Merrill, Wisconsin

Job Application
(Please Print)

PERSONAL

Name _Hughes_ _Connie_ _E_   Date _Jan. 6, 20--_
    Last   First   Middle

Address _304 Cottage St._ _Springtown_ _Co._ _81648_
    No. & Street   City   State   Zip

Telephone Number _(970) 920-4198_ Social Security Number _382-91-8206_

Person to call in case of emergency

James Adams _620 Pike St. Springtown_ _(970) 920-6839_
Name   Address   Telephone

POSITION

Position or type of work desired _Janitor's Helper_

Are you willing to work: (circle)   Fulltime (Part-time) Nights   Weekends

Date available for employment _Immediately_

Present salary or wage _None_   Salary or wage expected _going rate_

EDUCATION

Circle Highest   Grade School   High School   College
Grade Completed   1 2 3 4 5 6 7 8   9 10 11 (12)   1 2 3 4 5

	Name Of School	Complete Address	Year Entered	Year Left
Grade School	Franklin	115 Mill St. Springtown	19--	19--
High School	Washington	2925 Hopkins St. Springtown	19--	19--
College				

EMPLOYMENT

WORK EXPERIENCE (Full or Part-time) List last job first.

Name of Employer	Address	Date Started	Date Left	Reason for Leaving
Sharon tyler	805 Water St.	June 1, 19--	Sept 1, 19--	School started
John Cooper	115 Vine St.	June 1, 19--	Sept 2, 19--	School started

REFERENCES (Please list three.)

Name	Address	Business or Occupation	Phone Number
Mary Morgan	130 2nd St.	Principal	920-3547
Gloria Sann	116 4th Ave.	Supervisor Ward mft.	920-9384
Rev. Robert Wells	193 Main St.	Minister	920-7311

Signature

MATCHING: Match the words in Column 1 with the correct meaning in Column 2.

Column 1   Column 2

_____ 1. contact   A. place to apply for a job

_____ 2. personnel office   B. neat and in order

_____ 3. application   C. to finish

_____ 4. interview   D. true; right; proper

_____ 5. correct   E. a request for a job

_____ 6. sloppy   F. woman's name before marriage

_____ 7. tidy   G. one who has the legal care of a person

_____ 8. maiden name   H. look for; think something will happen

_____ 9. permanent   I. a person who will speak well of another who is applying for a job

_____ 10. applicant   J. careless; not neat

_____ 11. reference   K. to stop; to end

_____ 12. going rate   L. a pressing need

_____ 13. expect   M. to vist and talk with

_____ 14. guardian   N. whatever employer is paying for the job

_____ 15. emergency   O. a person who applies for a job

_____ 16. complete   P. to try to make another person agree or believe; to persuade firmly

_____ 17. convince   Q. to get in touch with a person

_____ 18. quit   R. lasting; not for a short time

MULTIPLE CHOICE: Select the one best answer

_____ 1. An application is   A. a form   B. an agreement   C. a defect.

_____ 2. The job application should be checked to see that it is

         A. compete   B. complete   C. incomplete.

_____ 3. A good job reference person would be

         A. your uncle   B. your sister   C. a past employer.

_____ 4. An example of information to include in an application notebook is

         A. Social Security Number   B. religion   C. number of brothers and sisters

_____ 5. An untidy application form means that it is

         A. sloppy   B. neat   C. correct.

TRUE or FALSE: Place a "T" for true and an "F" for false before each statement.

_____ 1. For most jobs, it is not necessary to fill out an application form.

_____ 2. Application forms for all companies are exactly the same.

_____ 3. Employers like workers who follow directions.

_____ 4. It is important to spell words correctly on the application.

_____ 5. Employment applications should be filled out completely.

_____ 6. If a question is not meant for the applicant, it should be left blank.

_____ 7. A former employer is where a person has worked before.

_____ 8. The applicant should have the names of two references.

_____ 9. References should be adults.

_____ 10. A person's brother would be a good reference.

SYLLABLES: Endings of words (suffixes) are syllables. Divide the following words into syllables.

Example: old / er   soft / est   month / ly

1. nearly _____   6. faster _____

2. doing _____   7. neatly _____

3. filling _____   8. called _____

4. filled _____   9. trying _____

5. needed _____   10. higher _____

SYLLABLES: Letters added to the front of words (prefixes) are syllables. Divide the following words into syllables.

Example: de / lay   dis / like   re / mind

1. mistake _____   6. unlike _____

2. before _____   7. always _____

3. include _____   8. today _____

4. supervisor _____   9. return _____

5. belong _____   10. unheard _____

ALPHABETICAL ORDER: Put the list of words below in alphabetical (ABC) order.

person   1. _____

personnel   2. _____

planning   3. _____

possible   4. _____

print   5. _____

places   6. _____

parts   7. _____

parents   8. _____

permanent   9. _____

phone   10. _____

physical   11. _____

pay   12. _____

probably   13. _____

putting   14. _____

possibly   15. _____

MISSING "O's":   Make a real word from each group of letters by adding one or two "O's".

Example: wrk - work   ft - foot

cntact   1. _____   bk   10. _____

ging   2. _____   nne   11. _____

persn   3. _____   phne   12. _____

thught   4. _____   bss   13. _____

thrw   5. _____   lk   14. _____

frms   6. _____   schls   15. _____

supervisr   7. _____   sprts   16. _____

slppy   8. _____   pr   17. _____

peple   9. _____   ffice   18. _____

BUYING AND SELLING:

Column 2 has a list of companies that make or change a product into another product. In Column 1 is a list of materials or products that these companies buy. In Column 3 is a list of materials that these companies sell. Match Columns 1 and 3 with Column 2. (The first one is done for you.)

Column 1		Column 2		Column 3
BUYS		COMPANY		SELLS
____	bricks	1. Merrill Tent & Awning Co.	____	tractors
____	upholstery	2. Quality Print, Inc.	____	cabinets
____	meat	3. Atwood Homes, Inc.	____	coats
____	apples	4. Honeybee Dairy Corporation	____	books
____	vinyl	5. P & H Roofing and Masonry, Inc.	____	herring
____	hides	6. Case Implement Corporation	____	lumber
_1_	canvas	7. Pine Ridge Restaurant	____	chimneys
____	gold	8. Fromm Furriers, Inc.	____	rings
____	limestone	9. Wisconsin Refining Corp.	____	leather
____	crude oil	10. East Side Greenhouses, Inc.	____	homes
____	trees	11. Wausau Leather Company	____	suitcases
____	yarn	12. Rib Mountain Quarries, Inc.	____	mittens
____	paper	13. Medford Knitting Mills, Inc.	____	flowers
____	cabbage	14. Ocean Fish Corporation	____	cheese
____	lumber	15. Miller Furniture Company	____	sofas
____	plywood	16. Custom Woodworking, Inc.	____	hamburgers
____	motors	17. Lincoln Loggers, Inc.	____	sauerkraut
____	clay	18. Ward Pottery Corporation	_1_	tents
____	pelts	19. Sun Valley Orchards, Inc.	____	crushed rock
____	fish	20. Michigan Canners, Inc.	____	cider
____	milk	21. Carolina Luggage Corporation	____	vases
____	bulbs	22. Phillips Jewelry, Inc.	____	gasoline

MISSING "A's":   Make a real word from each group of letters by adding one or two "A's".

Examples: fir - fair   live - alive

lst	1. _____		miden	7. _____
lern	2. _____		pplicnt	8. _____
ner	3. _____		ddress	9. _____
cre	4. _____		slry	10. _____
sme	5. _____		net	11. _____
fcts	6. _____		sttus	12. _____

MISSING "I's":   Make a real word from each group of letters by adding one or two "I's".

Examples: nk - ink   wrtng - writing

drect	1. _____		lvng	7. _____
offce	2. _____		relatve	8. _____
wsh	3. _____		gong	9. _____
fll	4. _____		dvorce	10. _____
dffer	5. _____		possble	11. _____
mstake	6. _____		physcal	12. _____

SYNONYMS, ANTONYMS, AND HOMONYMS:

Words that have the same or nearly the same meaning are synomyms. Words that have opposite meanings are antonyms. Words that sound alike, but have different meanings and are spelled differently are called homonyms. Place an "S" before synomyms, an "A" before antonyms, and an "H" before the homonyms below.

Example: __A__ work / play   __S__ simple / easy

_____	1. last / first		_____	7. cellar / seller
_____	2. worker / employee		_____	8. salary / pay
_____	3. correct / wrong		_____	9. open / close
_____	4. profit / prophet		_____	10. physical / mental
_____	5. break / brake		_____	11. remember / forget
_____	6. careful / careless		_____	12. single / married

ALPHABETICAL ORDER: Place the following list of jobs in alphabetical (ABC) order.

leather manufacturing worker   1. _____

cement block plant worker   2. _____

stone quarry worker   3. _____

highway construction worker   4. _____

paper mill worker   5. _____

truck driver   6. _____

child care worker   7. _____

foundry worker   8. _____

cashier   9. _____

water department worker   10. _____

firefighter   11. _____

street department worker   12. _____

COMPOUND WORDS: Compound words are formed by joining together two words. Draw a line between the two words that make a compound word in the following list.

Example: basket / ball

1. paycheck	10. handsome	19. firefighter
2. dishwasher	11. chalkboard	20. careless
3. childhood	12. underpaid	21. policewoman
4. withhold	13. backfire	22. northwest
5. fireplace	14. southwest	23. afternoon
6. overwork	15. overtime	24. however
7. housekeeper	16. friendship	25. somewhat
8. woodwork	17. sometime	26. policeman
9. bricklayer	18. downtown	27. workbook

ACTIVITY: Fill out the application form on the next page. You are applying for a job as a janitor at the Acme Manufacturing Company. Use your own name, address, and all other information about yourself. If you need help, check the completed form that is found earlier in this lesson.

ACME MANUFACTURING COMPANY
Merrill, Wisconsin

Job Application
(Please Print)

P E R S O N A L

Name _____ Date _____
Last   First   Middle

Address _____
No. & Street   City   State   Zip

Telephone Number _____ Social Security Number _____

Person to call in case of emergency.

_____

Name   Address   Telephone

P O S I T I O N

Position or type of work desired _____

Are you willing to work: (circle)   Fulltime Part-time Nights   Weekends

Date available for employment _____

Present salary or wage _____ Salary or wage expected _____

E D U C A T I O N

Circle Highest   Grade School   High School   College
Grade Completed   1 2 3 4 5 6 7 8   9 10 11 12   1 2 3 4 5

	Name Of School	Complete Address	Year Entered	Year Left
Grade School				
High School				
College				

E M P L O Y M E N T

WORK EXPERIENCE (Full or Part-time) List last job first.

Name of Employer	Address	Date Started	Date Left	Reason for Leaving

R E F E R E N C E S

REFERENCES (Please list three.)

Name	Address	Business or Occupation	Phone Number

Signature _____

QUESTIONS:

1. Why should careful thought and planning be used when filling out the employment application?

2. Why should the employment application be filled out completely?

3. Why is it important to be neat when filling out the employment application?

4. Who is a reference?

5. Why should the job applicant always follow directions on the employment application?

6. What is a permanent address?

7. Why is it important not to make mistakes on the employment application form?

LESSON 8. JOB INTERVIEW

Getting a job is one of the most important things a person does in life. To get a job one almost always has to go for a job interview. During the interview, the applicant tries to sell herself or himself to the employer. The interviewer will be looking for someone who can be of help and assistance to the employer and the business. The interview will probably be the first meeting between the person applying for a job and the person doing the hiring. The fifteen or thirty minutes that an applicant spends in an interview may decide whether he or she gets the job or whether it will go to someone else. Therefore, it is important to know what to expect during the interview. A person may be the best worker in the world, but unless the interviewer is convinced, someone else may be hired.

Before anyone gives a party or has a picnic, he/she must do some planning. It is the same with the interview. Although a person cannot know everything that will take place during the interview, one should have some idea of what to expect and how to act. Employers are often surprised at how many job seekers come to the interview without any preparation. It is important to remember than an employer does not hire someone because that person is looking for a job. Workers are hired because they are needed for the business.

There are many things that can be done to prepare for the interview. A prepared applicant will tend to make fewer mistakes and will feel more at ease during the interview. Most people will be somewhat nervous during an interview, but the more that is known about what to expect, the less nervous the applicant will be.

One thing the applicant can do before the interview is to request a job description of the job position. A job description is the employer's written explanation of the duties of the job.

Most employers like employees who are clean and neat. They feel that a clean, neat person will do work that is neat and proper. About the only way the job interviewer has to determine if someone is neat is by looking at him or her. It is foolish to lose out on a job because of sloppy or improper dress. The best rule to follow is to dress nicely, but simply. This is known as dressing modestly.

67

The kind of clothes someone selects for the interview may depend on what kind of work one wants to do. If a man is applying for a job as a dishwasher, he could wear a sport shirt and slacks. If he is applying for a job as a sales clerk, he may wear a suit and tie. It is important to use good common sense in dressing.

Anyone going for an interview should be well groomed. This should include having the hair combed, fingernails clean, and shoes shined. It would be a good idea to bathe or shower and wear clothes that are clean and pressed. The applicant should use moderation when wearing make-up, jewelry or cologne.

Before the interview, the person applying for a job should know the exact place and time for the interview. It probably would be wise to find where the company is located a day or two ahead of time so that the applicant will not be late for the appointment. Being late for an interview is probably the easiest way to lose out on a job. Employers do not like employees who are late for work. An employee who is late may hold up the work of other employees as well as give a bad impression of himself/herself. So if a person cannot be on time for an interview, the interviewer should be called and the reason for being late should be explained. Remember it is better to be fifteen minutes early for an appointment than to be fifteen minutes late.

Friends or relatives should never be taken to the interview. The employer is not interested in them. The employer may feel that people applying for jobs may be unable to work by themselves if they need to bring others with them. The best rule to follow here is to go alone.

It is a wise idea to plan for the interview. The applicant should know what types of questions the interviewer will ask. For example, the employer may want to know why the applicant wants to work for this company or why he is interested in a certain kind of work. The interviewer may ask what he has in mind for the future or why he left his last job. These are all important questions and the applicant should know the answers before the interview.

If possible, the applicant should know the name of the interviewer before the interview. It is also important to know something about the company before the appointment. It is easier to answer the interviewer's questions and to ask questions of the interviewer if one has an understanding of the company. Information about a company can be secured from present employees of the company, ads the company publishes, published company reports and from the Internet. Specific information about the job applied for can be found in the job description.

All the facts and information needed to answer the interviewer's questions as well as how to properly fill out the application form should be known by the person applying for the job. In one of the past lessons, a notebook for important information was discussed. This should be taken to the interview. Social Security cards as well as any other identification necessary for the job should also be taken to the interview. A pencil, paper, and a good black or blue pen are important tools for the job interview.

During the interview, it is important to be friendly and courteous. After entering the interviewer's office, the applicant should introduce himself or herself. The job being sought can also be stated. A man might say, "I'm Steve McBride and I'm here for the job of assembly-line worker." If the secretary introduces the applicant to the interviewer, it is wise to say "hello" and let the interviewer ask the first question or start the discussion. After the introduction the applicant should remain standing until the interviewer asks him/her to be seated. He should sit straight in the chair and pay close attention to the questions and instructions of the interviewer. All questions should be answered honestly. It is a mistake to talk too much or to brag about past jobs. It is important that the employer know as much as possible about the applicant from the interview.

If anyone applying for a job wishes more information about the work, it is okay to ask. There is nothing wrong with asking questions of the interviewer. This may show the employer that the applicant has a real interest in the job. Anger should never enter into the interview. A person who shows anger may never get the job.

After the interview, the applicant should thank the interviewer for his time and interest. This is very important even if one does not get the job. It is important to remember that the success of the interview and future interviews depends on how well the applicant sells himself or herself.

Perhaps the most important part of getting a job is the interview. If the job seeker has made it this far, the employment can be won or lost during the first ten minutes. Therefore, before you go for an interview, reread these pages, recheck your notebook, and review your facts. Then, sure of yourself and properly dressed, go and put your "best foot forward."

MATCHING: Match the words in Column 1 with the correct meaning in Column 2.

Column 1

_____ 1. interview

_____ 2. apply

_____ 3. expect

_____ 4. convince

_____ 5. job seeker

_____ 6. ease

_____ 7. interviewer

_____ 8. modestly

_____ 9. selects

_____ 10. groom

_____ 11. bathe

_____ 12. relative

_____ 13. courteous

_____ 14. introduction

_____ 15. anger

Column 2

A. look for; think something will happen

B. person looking for a job

C. chooses or picks out

D. polite

E. to take care of a person's appearance

F. face to face meeting with employer

G. feeling that someone has toward someone else

H. make a person feel sure of something

I. asking for a job

J. father, brother, sister, cousin

K. dressed nicely, but simply

L. making name known to another person

M. employer who interviews

N. take a bath

O. free of trouble or worry

INTERVIEW ACTIONS: Below is a list of things a person should do or should not do before or during an interview. Write the word <u>DO</u> before the statement if it is a good thing, and <u>DO NOT</u> before the statement if it is a poor thing to do.

_____ 1. get angry

_____ 2. listen carefully

_____ 3. plan ahead

_____ 4. be on time

_____ 5. brag about your last job

_____ 6. bring along facts

_____ 7. be clean and neat

_____ 8. pretend to know it all

_____ 9. ask good questions

_____ 10. thank the interviewer after the interview

_____ 11. chew gum

_____ 12. speak clearly

_____ 13. be honest

_____ 14. follow directions

_____ 15. be courteous

_____ 16. be friendly

_____ 17. sit straight

_____ 18. look pleasant

_____ 19. smoke cigarettes

_____ 20. let the interviewer lead the discussion

(continued)

INTERVIEW ACTIONS, continued   (Write the word <u>DO</u> before the statement if it is a good thing, and <u>DO NOT</u> before the statement if it is a poor thing to do.)

_____	21. answer question dishonestly	_____	31. wear a simple business suit
_____	22. answer questions clearly	_____	32. tell jokes
_____	23. wear a cocktail dress	_____	33. go alone
_____	24. interrupt the interviewer	_____	34. talk about your troubles
_____	25. wear flashy jewelry	_____	35. stand straight
_____	26. be modest in dress	_____	36. look at the interviewer
_____	27. know the interviewer's name	_____	37. sit when you are asked to do so
_____	28. keep hands under control	_____	38. be natural
_____	29. use slang language	_____	39. bathe and use deodorant
_____	30. be well groomed	_____	40. know something about the company

WORD SELECTION: Below there are four words in a row. Three of the words have the same meaning or go together. One word has a different meaning or does not go with the other three. Draw a line under the word that does not belong with the others.

	Example:	horse	sheep	monkey	<u>apple</u>

1.	job	occupation	employment	church
2.	person	plant	human	man
3.	interview	talk	fifteen	meeting
4.	employer	worker	applicant	employee
5.	mistake	error	incorrect	correct
6.	chooses	party	selects	picks
7.	angry	friendly	courteous	pleasant
8.	friend	mother	relative	sister
9.	seek	hunt	look	future
10.	sloppy	tidy	neat	orderly
11.	modest	brag	cocky	boast
12.	planning	preparation	arrange	sell
13.	nervous	neatness	tense	fearful
14.	relative	company	business	occupation
15.	restaurant	store	office	person

SPELLING: The following words are misspelled. Place the correct spelling on the line following the word.

1. hireing _____
2. convence _____
3. planing _____
4. interveiw _____
5. bussiness _____
6. perpared _____
7. modesthly _____

8. clothies _____
9. comnon _____
10. important _____
11. groommed _____
12. freind _____
13. aplicant _____
14. neccesary _____

ALPHABETICAL ORDER: Place the following words in alphabetical (ABC) order:

decide

interviewer

appointment

interview

relative

preparation

sense

remember

friendly

perfume

questions

future

applicant

published

identification

introduction

information

1. _____
2. _____
3. _____
4. _____
5. _____
6. _____
7. _____
8. _____
9. _____
10. _____
11. _____
12. _____
13. _____
14. _____
15. _____
16. _____
17. _____

QUESTIONS:

1. List five things a person should do during an interview.

   A. _____

   B. _____

   C. _____

   D. _____

   E. _____

2. List three things that should be planned before the interview.

   A. _____

   B. _____

   C. _____

3. List three questions that the employer might ask during the interview.

   A. _____

   B. _____

   C. _____

4. List three articles a person should bring along to the interview.

   A. _____

   B. _____

   C. _____

LESSON 9. FAILURE TO GET WORK

Employers hire people because they need them for their companies. No one is hired because the employer feels that the applicant needs the money. If the company has a job opening, it is for one of the following reasons:

1. Someone has quit.

2. Someone has retired.

3. Someone has been promoted to a better job.

4. Someone was fired or released.

5. Someone is ill or has had an accident.

6. The company may need more employees because it is making more products or providing more services.

When a person applies for a job, it is important to present oneself in such a way that the employer will want to hire him or her. The employer has to feel that the new employee is going to be of value to the company. If the company feels that the applicant is not right for the job, they will look for someone else.

This lesson will deal with the reasons people are not hired for a job. There are many reasons why interviewers do not hire certain people. Some of the reasons why certain people do not get a job are the following:

1. Sloppy and untidy appearance

One of the ways an interviewer judges an applicant is by the way the person looks and dresses. Is the hair combed, clothes pressed, shoes shined? A sloppy dresser may mean a sloppy worker to the interviewer.

2. Lack of training and experience

Many jobs require that the employee have certain skills before he or she can do the job. The employer who pays a worker expects that worker to have the necessary skills before he/she is hired. A plumber needs to go through a training program and gain some experience working under another plumber before being hired as a skilled employee. A carpenter or a machine lathe operator also needs experience or training.

A person might be trained for a job by taking certain vocational courses in high school, by attending night classes, by attending a vocational or technical school, or by learning on the job. Most interviewers like to see experienced applicants. This tells the interviewer that this worker probably was successful on a former job and has the necessary skills to handle the new job.

Sometimes the only way a person can gain experience on the job is to take one that does not require many skills and then work up into one that does. Sometimes this is a slow method, but many times it is the only way to success.

3. Lack of Education

Most companies today require that the people they hire must be high school graduates. There are more people without jobs in the high school dropout group than in any other group. Many employers feel that anyone who drops out of school is a person who cannot finish a job. They feel that if the individual could not finish high school, he/she probably would not last on the job either.

Today companies spend thousands of dollars to buy expensive machinery and equipment. They want people with an education to operate them. When a worker is hired for a job, he/she is expected to have the proper education to handle it.

4. Poor Attitude

When a company hires a worker, they expect that worker to do the job to the best of his/her ability. They expect that he/she will cooperate with the foreman or boss and will get along with fellow workers. Most jobs require that the worker behave in a courteous, friendly, and adult manner. The job seeker has to convince the interviewer that these responsibilities will be accepted.

Most companies try not to hire people with poor job attitudes. They want employees who are able to control themselves as well as get along with other people. More workers are fired because they have a poor job attitude than for any other reason.

5. Demand too much pay

Most companies have some kind of a pay scale that was formed by the employer and the employees or by the company and the union. The pay scale is generally based on the worker's experience, education, training, and type of work that he/she does. Starting workers generally must start on the bottom of the pay scale and work themselves up by gaining more training, experience, and skills.

If the job seeker demands a salary that is higher than the company's scale for a particular job, he/she may not get the job. It is best to start at the salary offered and hope to get raises by doing good work. Most employers treat good workers fairly.

6. Not Being Sure of the Type of Job Wanted

Many times job seekers will go to a personnel office and say they will take any work the company has to offer. Generally, this is a mistake. The applicant should have a job in mind and apply for that job. Interviewers do not care much for applicant's who need work so badly they will take any job. Although the applicant should have a definite job in mind, he/she should be willing to take suggestions about other kinds of work that the interviewer might offer.

7. Not Wanting To Start on the Bottom

When most companies hire new employees, they will get work that the other employees do not want. The other employees have worked themselves up from this type of work. Generally, these are the harder, dirtier, poorer paying jobs.

If the applicants are not willing to take these kinds of jobs, they may not find employment. Applicants should consider such jobs with the idea that they will work themselves up as the other employees in the company have done.

Remember that employers do not care for employees who expect to start at the "top of the ladder." The best way for employees to move up is to prove themselves on a job.

8. Poor work record

It takes several months or more to train an employee for a job in a company. The training time may cost the employer more than the employee contributes to the company. Therefore, employers do not like to hire people for their companies if they think these workers will be on the job for only a short while.

If a person has had several jobs in the past year or two, the interviewer may feel that the applicant is a poor employee risk. He/she may quit again just as in the past. The interviewer may also feel that the person is a poor worker or cannot get along with other people. The interviewer may think that the applicant has been released or fired from past jobs.

No matter what kind of work anyone does, it is important to do it well. Someday some future employer may be looking at the work record a person has made.

9. Poor References

Sometimes job seekers use the wrong people for references and, therefore, do not get the employment they want. Relatives should never be used for references. The interviewer may not believe too much of what a person's uncle says about him/her.

A good reference must know the applicant quite well. It is a mistake to use someone for a reference if that person cannot answer questions about the applicant. It is wise to select someone that the person knows will give him or her a good reference. Past employers, teachers, and ministers generally make good references. It is important to choose references carefully. It is very important to ask a person if you may use him or her as a reference before doing so.

MATCHING: Match the words in Column 1 with the correct meaning in Column 2.

	Column 1		Column 2
_____	1. promoted	A.	person who quits school before graduation
_____	2. experienced	B.	costs much money
_____	3. dropout	C.	way of thinking, acting, or feeling
_____	4. expensive	D.	knowledge gained by doing something
_____	5. cooperate	E.	give money or help
_____	6. adult	F.	let go; let loose
_____	7. attitude	G.	raise in rank, pay, or importance
_____	8. contribute	H.	mature; grown-up
_____	9. released	I.	work together
_____	10. reliable	J.	can be depended on; worthy of a person's trust

BLANKS: Use the following words to fill in the blanks.

graduates	hire	bottom	dresses	scale
experienced	attitude	education	finish	courteous

1. Employers _____ people because they need them.

2. One of the ways an interviewer judges an applicant is by the way that person

   _____ .

3. Most interviewers like to see _____ applicants.

4. Most companies today require that the people they hire must be high school

   _____ .

5. Many employers feel that a person who drops out of school is one who cannot

   _____ a job.

6. Employers want people with an _____ to operate their expensive machines and equipment.

7. Most jobs require that the worker behave in a _____ , friendly, and adult manner.

8. More workers are fired because they have a poor job _____ than for any other reason.

9. Most companies have some kind of a pay _____ that was formed by the employees and the employer.

10. Most employees have to start on the _____ of the work ladder.

SINGULAR/PLURAL:

When a naming word means only one, it is <u>singular</u>. When it means more than one, it is <u>plural</u>. Naming words that end in "y" are changed from singular to plural by adding either "s" or by changing the "y" to the "i" and adding "es". If the letter before the "y" is a vowel (a-e-i-o-u), "s" is added to make the word plural. If the letter before the "y" is a consonant, the "y" is changed to "i" and "es" is added. Change the following words from singular to plural.

Examples: key - keys   country - countries

company	1. _____	delay	11. _____
apply	2. _____	baby	12. _____
employ	3. _____	copy	13. _____
buy	4. _____	county	14. _____
ability	5. _____	turkey	15. _____
responsibility	6. _____	family	16. _____
pay	7. _____	reply	17. _____
story	8. _____	chimney	18. _____
lady	9. _____	fly	19. _____
way	10. _____	city	20. _____

SYNONYMS and ANTONYMS:

Words that have the same or nearly the same meaning are <u>synonyms</u>. Words that have opposite or nearly opposite meanings are <u>antonyms</u>. Place an "S" before the synonyms and an "A" before the antonyms in the following list.

_____	1.	hire	fire	_____	11.	delight	please
_____	2.	open	close	_____	12.	many	few
_____	3.	ill	sick	_____	13.	finish	quit
_____	4.	quit	start	_____	14.	buy	sell
_____	5.	more	less	_____	15.	foreman	boss
_____	6.	new	old	_____	16.	occupation	job
_____	7.	tell	ask	_____	17.	dirty	clean
_____	8.	fired	discharged	_____	18.	start	begin
_____	9.	weak	strong	_____	19.	train	instruct
_____	10.	dim	hazy	_____	20.	present	past

JOB ATTITUDES:

A job attitude is a worker's thinking, acting, or feeling toward work, employer, and fellow workers. If he/she always does his/her best, or tries to be a good worker, he/she has a good job attitude. If he/she is always looking for ways to get out of work or not do much, then he/she has a poor job attitude.

In the following list place a checkmark (√) before each item that would be a good job attitude.

_____	1.	cares for the job	_____	16.	talks back
_____	2.	is a careful worker	_____	17.	wastes material
_____	3.	tries to improve	_____	18.	looks clean and neat
_____	4.	is lazy	_____	19.	is loud and noisy
_____	5.	is cooperative	_____	20.	is dependable
_____	6.	does not listen	_____	21.	only wants the paycheck
_____	7.	tries his/her best	_____	22.	starts arguments
_____	8.	lies to people	_____	23.	follows directions
_____	9.	steals or cheats	_____	24.	has good manners
_____	10.	wastes time	_____	25.	minds own business
_____	11.	wants to succeed	_____	26.	does as he/she pleases
_____	12.	is willing to work	_____	27.	likes to sit around
_____	13.	gets along with others	_____	28.	picks on others
_____	14.	takes orders	_____	29.	is reliable
_____	15.	is often late for work	_____	30.	is loyal

TRUE or FALSE: Place a "T" for true and an "F" for false before each statement.

_____ 1. Everyone gets a job if he or she applies for it.

_____ 2. Training for some jobs could be learned by going to night classes.

_____ 3. It is easy for a high school dropout to find a job.

_____ 4. A worker should be able to get along with his/her fellow workers.

_____ 5. A good worker should cooperate with the boss.

_____ 6. The amount of pay a worker will get will depend partly on that worker's experience.

_____ 7. Many times the beginning worker must start at the bottom of the pay scale.

_____ 8. Many beginning workers start at the top of the "work ladder."

_____ 9. A job should always be done well.

_____ 10. A person's uncle makes a good reference.

TYPES OF JOBS: Following is a list of kinds of work employees must do on their job. Place the kind of work under the proper job.

1. scrape wood siding
2. sweep floors
3. sew on buttons
4. use chain saw
5. wash windows
6. shovel snow

7. putty windows
8. peel potatoes
9. mix dough
10. mark merchandise
11. make sandwiches
12. pack packages

13. iron clothes
14. mix paint
15. measure logs
16. sort clothes
17. limb trees
18. stock shelves

Forestry Worker

1. _____
2. _____
3. _____

Painter's Helper

1. _____
2. _____
3. _____

Janitor

1. _____
2. _____
3. _____

Cook's Helper

1. _____
2. _____
3. _____

Stock Person

1. _____
2. _____
3. _____

Laundry Worker

1. _____
2. _____
3. _____

The following list contains ten things that make a good worker. Place a checkmark (√) before the five you think are the most important for a good worker.

_____ 1. Is neat and clean

_____ 2. Is always happy and cheerful

_____ 3. Always does work carefully

_____ 4. Always uses the best language

_____ 5. Shows an interest in work

_____ 6. Never misses work

_____ 7. Is willing to learn new things about the job

_____ 8. Gets along with fellow workers

_____ 9. Always does his/her share of the work

_____ 10. Gets along with the boss or supervisor

WORD ENDINGS: The following are endings for words:

er	ment	ish
s	ly	es
ness	ing	less
en	th	ed
able	ful	

Place one of the endings on each of the following words to make a real word. Sometimes there are several correct answers, but you need only give one.

1. employ _____

2. mistake _____

3. nervous _____

4. most _____

5. neat _____

6. appoint _____

7. depend _____

8. press _____

9. friend _____

10. reference _____

11. seek _____

12. gain _____

13. wear _____

14. thank _____

15. four _____

16. fool _____

17. publish _____

18. help _____

19. fast _____

20. skill _____

21. class _____

22. state _____

23. success _____

24. release _____

PROBLEMS AND QUESTIONS:

1.   List five reasons why employers hire workers.

     A. _____

     B. _____

     C. _____

     D. _____

     E. _____

2.   List eight reasons why some people are not hired for a job.

     A. _____

     B. _____

     C. _____

     D. _____

     E. _____

     F. _____

     G. _____

     H. _____

3.   How could one get more training for a job?

4.   Explain the following statement: "Employees must be able to control themselves."

5.   Why is it important to do a job well?

LESSON 10. WORK PERMITS

In the early history of the United States, the use of child labor was common in the factories. It was not uncommon to find eight to fifteen year old boys and girls working in these factories. In 1646, factories built in Jamestown, Virginia, employed seven and eight-year-old boys and girls in the manufacture of linen cloth. Jamestown was the first permanent settlement of the English in America.

It was not uncommon to find children working fourteen to eighteen hours per day in the cotton mills during the 1700's. At this time in history, many people worked as much as seventy or eighty hours per week. There were few labor laws. During the early 1800's, many people began to complain about the use of children as laborers in these mills. At this time, many people started to ask for laws that would stop these employers from using young children for long hours. There was no question that these working children were unable to develop their bodies and minds as they should.

By the middle of the 1800's there was a feeling that children should be in school where they could grow and develop their minds rather than work in factories. At this time in history, some states were passing laws regulating working conditions. Some states passed laws requiring that young people had to be a certain age before they could go to work. At the same time, laws were being passed that allowed young people to work only a certain number of hours.

Over the years, the labor laws of the United States have become stronger. During this time, laws have been passed that require that young people attend school. Today the United States, as well as individual states, has many laws regulating working conditions for all people, including the young.

Today, many young people complain when they have to get a work permit to get a job. They feel it would be so much easier if they could take any job they wished. If everyone realized how child labor was misused during the history of our country, it would be easy to understand why there is a need for labor laws.

The labor laws in the fifty states of the United States differ from one another, but most of the states have many of the same requirements for getting a work permit. In some states, work permits are called "working papers." In this lesson, these general requirements will be discussed. It may be important for young workers to find out what the specific laws are in their states.

Most states require that anyone who employs a person under eighteen years of age, (in some states, sixteen years of age) must get a work permit for the employee. Even if married or a high school graduate, one must have the permit if he/she is less than eighteen years of age. Generally, permits are not given to young people less than fourteen years old, except for work in high school cafeterias, for paper routes, and a few other jobs. Work permits are generally not required for work on a family farm, for domestic work, or for volunteer work.

Work permits are issued by permit offices in most cities. A person's teacher, guidance counselor, principal, or his/her friends may know the location of permit offices. Two common places where work permits are issued are area high schools and county courthouses.

When applying for a permit, the following information for the permit office must be available:

1. Proof of age. This can be a copy of the birth certificate or baptismal record.

2. A letter from the employer stating that the applicant will be hired. This letter should include the kind of work that will be done and the hours and days to be worked.

3. A letter from the parent or guardian giving permission to work.

4. Social Security number.

5. A required fee. (The fee is different in different parts of the United States.)

6. Some states require a health certificate from a doctor before a permit is given.

It is important to remember that an employer must possess a work permit before hiring anyone under eighteen years of age.

MATCHING: Match the words in Column 1 with the correct meaning in Column 2.

Column 1

Column 2

_____   1.   manufacture

A.   definite; particular one; exact

_____   2.   linen

B.   refers to the home or work in a home

_____   3.   settlement

C.   making a new home in a new country

_____   4.   complain

D.   to control by rule or law

_____   5.   develop

E.   sacrament or rite that takes a person into the church

_____   6.   regulate

F.   make an article with labor and machine

_____   7.   specific

G.   to hold; to own; to have in one's hands

_____   8.   domestic

H.   say something is wrong; finding fault with something

_____   9.   location

I.   to allow; to let; to consent

_____   10.   baptism

J.   the exact position of the place

_____   11.   possess

K.   cloth made from flax

_____   12.   permission

L.   written or printed statement that may be used as proof of some fact

_____   13.   fee

M.   to grow; to get bigger or better

_____   14.   certificate

N.   a charge; money paid for a service

PREFIXES: The prefix "un" before a word may mean "not" as in the word <u>unable</u>. The prefix "mis" before a word may mean "bad" or "wrong" as in the word <u>miscount</u>. The prefix "re" before a word may mean "again" as in the word <u>reopen</u>.

Place one of the prefixes (un - mis - re) before the following words to make a real word.

1.   _____use

6.   _____deed

11.   _____lock

2.   _____work

7.   _____bend

12.   _____lead

3.   _____hire

8.   _____even

13.   _____spell

4.   _____common

9.   _____take

14.   _____print

5.   _____build

10.   _____born

15.   _____paid

BLANKS: Fill in the blanks with the correct word from the following list -

develop   attend   settlement   offices   permission
domestic   uncommon   fee   birth   possess

1. Jamestown was the first permanent _____ of the English in America.

2. In the early history of the United States, child labor was not _____ .

3. Working children could not _____ their minds and bodies as they should have been developed.

4. Laws were passed that required that young people _____ school.

5. In most states, a _____ is required to get a work permit.

6. Work permits are generally not required for _____ work.

7. A _____ certificate is good for proof of age.

8. An employer must _____ a work permit before allowing a young person to work.

9. Work permits are issued by permit _____ .

10. A person's parents or guardian must give their _____ before a work permit can be secured.

TRUE or FALSE: Place a "T" for true and an "F" for false before each statement.

_____ 1. All fifty states have exactly the same labor laws.

_____ 2. Some children worked fourteen to eighteen hours per day during the 1700's.

_____ 3. Over the years, labor laws in the United States have become stronger.

_____ 4. A seventeen year old married person does not need a work permit.

_____ 5. Permit offices are found in most United States cities.

_____ 6. A Social Security number is not needed to get a work permit.

_____ 7. Before a person can get a work permit, he/she must have a letter from the employer.

_____ 8. A Social Security card is a good proof of age for securing a work permit.

_____ 9. A person needs a work permit to do volunteer work.

_____ 10. A ten-year-old child can get a work permit.

SPELLING WORDS: Correct the misspelled words.

1. manfacture   _____
2. quastion   _____
3. complin   _____
4. schol   _____
5. disscus   _____

6. maried   _____
7. offics   _____
8. cafteria   _____
9. volunter   _____
10. ussualy   _____

SPELLING WORDS:

On each line below are four words from the lesson. Only one of the four is spelled correctly. Underline the correct one. The first one is done for you.

1.	oncommon	<u>uncommon</u>	oncomon	uncomon
2.	fifteen	fivteen	fiveteen	fiften
3.	permenant	permanant	permanent	premanent
4.	laborrs	labores	laboers	laborers
5.	develup	develop	develope	devulop
6.	condetion	condshion	condishion	condition
7.	sertain	certain	sertian	certian
8.	individual	endividual	individaul	indivaduel
9.	realizd	reelazed	realized	reelized
10.	greduate	gradute	graduat	graduate
11.	permit	permmit	premit	premmit
12.	divisian	divisan	division	divison
13.	genaral	ganeral	genarel	general
14.	dometic	domestic	domestix	domistec
15.	principel	principil	principal	principl
16.	remenber	remember	remimber	renember
17.	different	diferent	diferant	defferant
18.	guidence	guadence	giudance	guidance

BUYING AND SELLING:

Column 2 has a list of companies that make or change a product into another product. In Column 1 is a list of materials or products that these companies buy. In Column 3 is a list of products that these companies sell.

Match Columns 1 and 3 with Column 2. (The first one is done for you.)

Column 1 BUYS	Column 2 COMPANY	Column 3 SELLS
_____ copper	1. Atlas Milling Company	_____ windows
_____ cement	2. Ace Dairy Company	_____ lumber
_____ film	3. Western Textile Corporation	_____ portraits
_____ rubber	4. Meyer Slaughtering Company	_____ shoes
_____ cattle	5. Starlite Steel Corporation	_____ bread
_____ cream	6. Modern Baking Company	_1_ flour
_____ iron ore	7. Butler Furniture Company	_____ linen
_____ leather	8. Central Rubber Supply	_____ sheet metal
_____ flowers	9. Merrill Daily Tribune	_____ tires
_____ corn	10. High Top Footwear Corp.	_____ corsages
_____ logs	11. Merrill Woolen Knitting Mills	_____ corn flakes
_____ flour	12. Ace Photographers	_____ steaks
_1_ wheat	13. Bill's Florist Shop	_____ ice cream
_____ cheese	14. Johnson Construction Company	_____ candy
_____ lumber	15. General Cereal Company	_____ newspapers
_____ newsprint	16. Northern Window Corp.	_____ pizza
_____ eggs	17. National Copper Corp.	_____ paper
_____ chocolate	18. Acme Forest Products Corp.	_____ electric wire
_____ wood	19. Lincoln County Hatchery	_____ concrete
_____ glass	20. Queenie's Pizza, Inc.	_____ chairs
_____ flax	21. Palm's Candy Company	_____ sweaters
_____ wool	22. Wausau Paper Mills	_____ chicks

PROBLEMS AND QUESTIONS:

1. List five requirements for a work permit.

   A. _____

   B. _____

   C. _____

   D. _____

   E. _____

2. Explain why child labor laws were passed.

3. What kind of jobs do not require a work permit?

4. Where would you go for a work permit?

5. What can you use to prove your age?

6. Why do you think some states require a health certificate from a doctor before a work permit is given?

LESSON 11. FEDERAL INCOME TAX

Whenever services are provided by the government, the government gets the money to pay for the service by collecting taxes. Most of the money comes from taxes that are paid by workers and companies. Much of the money that the federal government gets comes from the federal income tax. An income tax is a tax that a worker pays on the amount of money earned. The greater the amount of money earned, the greater the tax. Generally, the amount of income tax a person pays is based on the amount earned and the number of people that the worker supports. A person who is supported by the worker is called a "dependent."

The federal income tax is sometimes referred to as a "withholding tax." This means that the money is held back or deducted from the worker's paycheck. When a person is paid for work, the employer takes off a certain amount and sends it to the Internal Revenue Service (IRS). The Internal Revenue Service is the department of the federal government that collects the income taxes that are paid.

Taxes are as old as civilized man. During the time of the emperors of ancient Rome, there were tax collectors who collected money from the people to pay for running the government. During the early history of the United States, taxes were an important part of life. In fact, an important reason that the early American Colonists fought the war for American Independence was taxes. The colonists felt they were being taxed unfairly.

It was once said that taxes are what is paid for a civilized society. If the people felt that they did not want any services from the government, there would be no need for taxes. Yet many times people want more and more services from the government, but would rather not pay the taxes. People probably talk and complain about taxes as often as they talk and complain about the weather.

The money that the government collects from taxes is used to provide many public services. A large part of the money that the government collects in taxes goes to pay for the national defense of the country. If there were no taxes, there would be no way of paying for our Army, Navy, Air Force, or Marine Corps. The federal government also spends money for international affairs such as the military aid and foreign aid programs. The costs of the flights to outer space are paid by the federal treasury.

The government also spends money for soil conservation, inspection of the food people eat, flood control along the rivers of the United States, and keeping up the national forests and parks that the government owns.

The federal treasury helps provide loans and grants for housing and homes for the aged and for those people who cannot afford to buy a home without help. The government pays for some types of vocational education, manpower training, medical research, and medical bills of the aged and the poor in the country.

Other programs paid for by the federal government are medical care, education, life insurance benefits and pension benefits for veterans of the United States Armed Forces.

There are many more services that are provided by the government that are not mentioned here. It is important to remember that all services of the government must be paid for by the taxpayers of the United States. Without taxes, these services would not be available.

After taking a job, one of the first responsibilities of a worker is to fill out an "Employee's Withholding Allowance Certificate." This form is also known as Form W-4. This certificate is necessary so that the employer knows how much tax should be withheld from the worker's paycheck. Remember that the amount of tax is based on the amount earned and the number of dependents a worker has claimed. There is one exemption for the worker and one for each of his/her dependents. For example, a married man with three children would have five exemptions. These would include one for himself, one for his wife, and one for each of his children. A young single person will have only one exemption for himself unless he is supporting his parents or someone else.

People living at home cannot claim one exemption for themselves if their parents claim them as one exemption. Dependents do not get a personal exemption if they are claimed as dependents on another person's tax return. It is unlawful to claim more exemptions than a worker has a right to claim.

If one person is working at two jobs at the same time, an exemption should be claimed on only one job. No exemptions should be claimed on the other job. For example, a person might be working as a plumber's helper during the day and washing dishes in a cafeteria for two hours during the evening. One exemption should be claimed on the plumber's job and zero (0) exemptions on the cafeteria job.

The employer will give Form W-4 to the employee. When a person starts a job, the employer will ask that it be filled out.

Following is a properly filled out Form W-4 for a single worker. Notice that it is all printed except the signature.

Form **W-4** Department of the Treasury Internal Revenue Service	**Employee's Withholding Allowance Certificate** ▶ For Privacy Act and Paperwork Reduction Act Notice, see page 2.	OMB No. 1545-0010

1 Type or print your first name and middle initial **Mark J.**	Last name **Adams**	2 Your social security number **486-00-9312**

Home address (number and street or rural route) **705 Oak Street**	3 ☒ Single ☐ Married ☐ Married, but withhold at higher Single rate. Note: If married, but legally separated, or spouse is a nonresident alien, check the Single box.
City or town, state, and ZIP code **Goodrich, MI 49445**	4 If your last name differs from that on your social security card, check here. You must call 1-800-772-1213 for a new card .... ▶ ☐

5	Total number of allowances you are claiming (from line H above or from the worksheets on page 2 if they apply)	5	**1**
6	Additional amount, if any, you want withheld from each paycheck......................................	6	$
7	I claim exemption from withholding for 1999, and I certify that I meet BOTH of the following conditions for exemption:		
	● Last year I had a right to a refund of ALL Federal income tax withheld because I had NO tax liability AND		
	● This year I expect a refund of ALL Federal income tax withheld because I expect to have NO tax liability.		
	If you meet both conditions, enter "EXEMPT" here .... ▶	7	

Under penalties of perjury, I certify that I am entitled to the number of withholding allowances claimed on this certificate, or I am entitled to claim exempt status.

Employee's signature
(Form is not valid
unless you sign it) ▶ *Mark J. Adams*   Date ▶ **2-20-20··**

8 Employer's name and address (Employer: Complete 8 and 10 only if sending to the IRS)	9 Office code (optional)	10 Employer identification number

ISA

During the time a person works for an employer, the employer will withhold federal income tax and send it to the government. Sometime during the month of January, the employer will send a "Wage and Tax Statement" to the worker. This statement is also known as Form W-2. If the worker had more than one job during the year, the worker will receive a Form W-2 from each employer. Form W-2 is an important paper and should be kept in a safe place until the worker is ready to file the tax forms.

The Form W-2 will give the following information:

1. The amount of wages or salary the worker earned for the past year.

2. The amount of federal income taxes withheld from the person's pay during the past year.

3. The amount of Social Security tax (F.I.C.A.) withheld from the worker's pay during the past year.

The Wage and Tax Statement is an important paper. One copy must be included when filing a federal income tax form. One copy is kept for the worker's records. One copy is sent to the Internal Revenue Service by the employer.

Following is a Form W-2 that a worker received from an employer.

a Control number		OMB No. 1545-0008		
b Employer's identification number 392-26-1975			1 Wages, tips, other compensation $8,100.00	2 Federal income tax withheld $405.00
c Employer's name, address, and ZIP code			3 Social security wages $8,100.00	4 Social security tax withheld $502.20
Acme Laundry 1256 Pine Street Goodrich, MI 49445			5 Medicare wages and tips $8,100.00	6 Medicare tax withheld $117.45
			7 Social security tips	8 Allocated tips
d Employee's social security number 486-00-9512			9 Advance EIC payment	10 Dependent care benefits
e Employee's name, address, and ZIP code			11 Nonqualified plans	12 Benefits included in box 1
Mark J. Adams 705 Oak Street Goodrich, MI 49445			13	14 Other
			15 Statutory employee ☐ Deceased ☐ Pension plan ☐ Legal rep. ☐ Deferred compensation ☐	

16 State Employer's state I.D. no. MI	17 State wages, tips, etc. $8,100.00	18 State income tax $233.20	19 Locality name	20 Local wages, tips, etc.	21 Local income tax

Form W-2 Wage and Tax Statement

Department of the Treasury — Internal Revenue Service

Sometime between the time a worker gets a Form W-2 from the employer and April 15, he/she may file an income tax form. This form is known as Form 1040, Form 1040A, or Form 1040EZ, and may be obtained from the Internal Revenue Service or from most post offices. Form 1040 is the longest form, Form 1040A is a shorter form, and 1040EZ is the shortest form. Most beginning workers will file Form 1040EZ.

If a worker owes no income tax and some taxes were withheld from earnings, the worker will get the amount withheld returned if Form 1040, Form 1040A, or Form 1040EZ is filed by April 15th. If the worker owes less than was withheld, some will be returned if Form 1040, Form 1040A, or Form1040EZ is filed. Remember that a copy of the Form W-2 must be attached to Form 1040, Form 1040A, or Form 1040EZ when it is filed. The federal treasury will send a check to taxpayers who have paid too much in taxes. Some of the information used to file either Form 1040, Form 1040A, or Form 1040EZ comes from the Form W-2. If the worker owes additional taxes, the Internal Revenue Service will figure the tax and send the taxpayer a bill. If a worker chooses to figure the tax, he/she should mail a check covering the additional tax owed to the Internal Revenue Service. This should be mailed with Form 1040, Form 1040A, or Form 1040EZ.

Beginning workers may find friends or relatives who will help them file their tax forms for the first few years. There are also many people and businesses who help people file income tax forms in most communities of the Unites States. Many of these individuals and businesses advertise their services in newspapers, on radio, and on television. There is a charge for this service, but for the beginning worker, the charge is generally small.

Your teacher may give you more information and forms that will help explain federal income taxes. These materials can be secured by writing to the Internal Revenue Service. Most of these materials are free.

It is important to know how to file a tax return. When a person starts working, federal income taxes will be withheld from the worker's paycheck. It may be against the law if a person does not file a tax form by April 15th.

MATCHING: Match the words in Column 1 with the correct meaning in Column 2.

Column 1

_____ 1. tax

_____ 2. federal

_____ 3. dependent

_____ 4. emperor

_____ 5. collector

_____ 6. civilized

_____ 7. defense

_____ 8. international

_____ 9. inspection

_____ 10. treasury

_____ 11. exemption

_____ 12. withheld

_____ 13. claim

_____ 14. file

Column 2

A. a person who is supported by another

B. a person hired to collect taxes

C. hold back; keep back

D. the change from being savage and ignorant to having good laws and customs

E. protect or guard the nation

F. money paid by people for support of the government

G. look over carefully; examine

H. a place where money is kept

I. refers to the central government of the U.S.

J. between or among nations

K. make free; make free from taxes

L. a man who is the ruler of an empire

M. to demand as a person's right; the right to demand something

N. turn income tax papers into the government

TRUE or FALSE: Place a "T" for true and an "F" for false before each statement.

_____ 1. Services provided by the government are paid for by taxes.

_____ 2. An income tax is tax on a person's home.

_____ 3. The amount of income tax a person pays will depend on the amount earned and the number of dependents.

_____ 4. The federal income tax is a withholding tax.

_____ 5. The Internal Revenue Service collects income taxes.

_____ 6. People in ancient Rome paid no taxes.

_____ 7. The early American Colonists paid no taxes.

_____ 8. Taxes are what is paid for a civilized society.

_____ 9. The government collects taxes to help pay for the national defense of the country.

_____ 10. Benefits to veterans are paid with money from federal income taxes.

_____ 11. A person should always claim at least one exemption on Form W-2.

_____ 12. Form W-2 is filled out by the worker.

_____ 13. The employee will receive a Form W-2 during the month of January.

_____ 14. Everyone must file Income Tax Form 1040A.

_____ 15. Income tax forms must be filed on or before April 15th.

MULTIPLE CHOICE: Select the one best answer.

_____ 1. Federal income tax is a tax on --

    (A)   a home   (B)   a new suit   (C)   money earned

_____ 2. The federal income tax is also known as --

    (A)   a withholding tax   (B)   an excise tax   (C)   a real estate tax

_____ 3. A person who is supported by another person is called --

    (A)   a colonist   (B)   a dependent   (C)   an independent

_____ 4. Taxes are used to pay for --

    (A)   national defense   (C)   both of these
    (B)   trips to outer space

_____ 5. An "Employee's Withholding Allowance Certificate" is known as --

    (A)   Form W-2   (B)   Form W-4   (C)   Form 1040A

_____ 6. A married man with four children will probably claim no more than --

    (A)   one exemption   (C)   six exemptions
    (B)   four exemptions

_____ 7. The "Wage and Tax Statement" is known as --

    (A)   Form W-2   (B)   Form W-4   (C)   Form 1040A

_____ 8. The best place to get Form 1040EZ would be --

    (A)   at a post office
    (B)   from a teacher
    (C)   at a discount store

_____ 9. Form W-2 is mailed or given to an employee during the month of --

    (A)   January   (C)   November
    (B)   June

_____ 10. A single person who completely supports one parent could claim

    (A)   one exemption
    (B)   two exemptions
    (C)   no exemptions

SPELLING: Correct the misspelled words. (Continued on the following page.)

1. recieved _____   4. cliam _____

2. statment _____   5. dishs _____

3. includ _____   6. taxs _____

7. incone   _____   11. dependants   _____

8. servics   _____   12. remenber   _____

9. runing   _____   13. withold   _____

10. federel   _____   14. selary   _____

BLANKS: Place the following words in the proper blanks.

department	civilized	affairs
grants	Form W-4	collects
deducted	earned	treasury
exemption		

1. The money that the government _____ from taxes is used to provide many public services.

2. An income tax is a tax that a worker pays on the amount of money that is _____.

3. The Internal Revenue Service is the _____ of the federal government that collects income taxes.

4. The cost of the flights to outer space are paid by the federal _____.

5. Federal income tax is _____ from a worker's earnings.

6. Taxes are what is paid for a _____ society.

7. The federal government spends money for international _____.

8. The federal treasury helps provide loans and _____ for housing and homes for the aged.

9. Workers can claim one _____ for themselves and one for each dependent.

10. When a person starts a job, the employer will ask that a _____ be filled out.

MISSING LETTERS: Place the missing letter or letters in the blank spaces.

1. A Form 1040A may be ob __ ain __ d from the In __ __ __ nal Revenue Ser __ ice.

2. Most of the mon __ y that the f __ __ eral treasury receives comes from

    in __ ome taxes paid by w __ __ kers and comp __ nies.

3. Taxes are as old as civ __ l __ zed man.

(continued on next page)

4. An im __ ort __ nt reason the e __ __ ly American Colonists f __ __ ght the war for

    in __ epen __ ence was be __ ause of taxes.

5. The govern __ ent sp __ nds money for so __ l con __ ervation, fo __ d in __ pection,

    and flo __ d con __ __ ol.

6. The amount of income t __ x a pe __ son pays is based on the a __ ou __ t earned and

    the n __ __ ber of people that the worker su __ ports.

7. The f __ d __ ral income tax is somet __ mes refer __ ed to as a with __ oldi __ g tax.

SELECTING TOOLS AND SUPPLIES:

In Column 1 is a list of jobs. Columns 2, 3, and 4 list tools and supplies required on these jobs. Select the correct tools and supplies necessary for each of the jobs. The first one is done for you.

	Column 1	Column 2	Column 3	Column 4
1.	dishwasher	soap	water	pencils
2.	welder	leather gloves	gasoline	rods
3.	mason	trowels	flowers	cement
4.	rodeo rider	brooms	chaps	spurs
5.	typist	paint	typewriter	paper
6.	baker	flour	salt	lumber
7.	auto mechanic	cleaning solvent	clippers	wrenches
8.	sales clerk	cash register	flour	paper
9.	forestry worker	axes	saws	brushes
10.	roofer	thermometer	hammers	nails
11.	photographer	camera	film	grease
12.	barber	staplers	clippers	scissors
13.	soldier	bayonet	putty	rifle
14.	firefighter	ladders	axes	cement
15.	painter	pipe	brushes	scrapers

JOBS AND SPEECH: In Column 1 are jobs people perform. In Column 2 are kinds of language people would use while working at these jobs. Match Column 1 with Column 2. (The first one is done for you.)

Column 1   Column 2

_T_   1. dairywoman   A.   you have a slight fever

_____ 2. usher   B.   the ceiling should be white

_____ 3. teacher   C.   lower the nets

_____ 4. baker   D.   the news deadline is three o'clock

_____ 5. typist   E.   the oil gauge shows full

_____ 6. painter   F.   do not pick green tomatoes

_____ 7. parking lot attendant   G.   park the Ford in the first stall

_____ 8. filing clerk   H.   the stone is one carat

_____ 9. service station attendant   I.   smile

_____ 10. plumber   J.   please sit in the front row

_____ 11. fisherman   K.   run up the center

_____ 12. seamstress   L.   the turf should be watered

_____ 13. vegetable picker   M.   stay in shallow water

_____ 14. jeweler   N.   sugar the doughnuts

_____ 15. reporter   O.   the children behaved well

_____ 16. soldier   P.   take out your paper and pencil

_____ 17. golf course worker   Q.   coffee, tea, or milk

_____ 18. doctor   R.   the roast should be baked for two hours

_____ 19. cook's helper   S.   this typewriter does not work

_____ 20. babysitter   T.   milk should be cooled to 40° F

_____ 21. photographer   U.   plastic tubing is cheaper than copper

_____ 22. coach   V.   the hem should be lowered

_____ 23. lifeguard   W.   the rifle is clean

_____ 24. waitress   X.   the folders are in ABC order

PROBLEMS AND QUESTIONS:

1.   List three kinds of information found on the Form W-2.

   A. _____

   B. _____

   C. _____

2.   What is the Internal Revenue Service?

3.   Who is a dependent?

4.   Why does the government collect taxes?

5.   Who collects the federal income tax?

6.   List five things the government pays for with tax money.

   A. _____

   B. _____

   C. _____

   D. _____

   E. _____

7.   When does a worker fill out Form W-4?

8.   When should a worker claim zero (0) exemptions on Form W-4?

9.   Where does a worker get a Form W-4?

10. How many "Wage and Tax Statements" will a worker receive each year?

ACTIVITIES:

1. Below is an "Employee's Withholding Allowance Certificate," Form W-4. Fill it out just as if you were starting on a job today. Look back at the example in the lesson if you need help.

Form **W-4**	**Employee's Withholding Allowance Certificate**	OMB No. 1545-0010
Department of the Treasury Internal Revenue Service	▶ For Privacy Act and Paperwork Reduction Act Notice, see page 2.	

1 Type or print your first name and middle initial	Last name	2 Your social security number

Home address (number and street or rural route)	3 ☐ Single ☐ Married ☐ Married, but withhold at higher Single rate.
	Note: If married, but legally separated, or spouse is a nonresident alien, check the Single box.
City or town, state, and ZIP code	4 If your last name differs from that on your social security card, check here. You must call 1-800-772-1213 for a new card .... ▶ ☐

5	Total number of allowances you are claiming (from line H above or from the worksheets on page 2 if they apply)	5	
6	Additional amount, if any, you want withheld from each paycheck	6 $	
7	I claim exemption from withholding for 1999, and I certify that I meet **BOTH** of the following conditions for exemption:		

- Last year I had a right to a refund of **ALL** Federal income tax withheld because I had **NO** tax liability **AND**
- This year I expect a refund of **ALL** Federal income tax withheld because I expect to have **NO** tax liability.

If you meet both conditions, enter "EXEMPT" here .... ▶ | 7 |

Under penalties of perjury, I certify that I am entitled to the number of withholding allowances claimed on this certificate, or I am entitled to claim exempt status.

Employee's signature
(Form is not valid
unless you sign it) ▶   Date ▶

8 Employer's name and address (Employer: Complete 8 and 10 only if sending to the IRS)	9 Office code (optional)	10 Employer identification number

ISA

2. You have received the following "Wage and Tax Statement," Form W-2 from your employer. Your job is a janitor's helper. Fill out the Individual Income Tax Return Form 1040A that is given you by your teacher. Use the information from Form W-2 below.

a Control number		OMB No. 1545-0008		
b Employer's identification number 392-00-0000			1 Wages, tips, other compensation $6,760.00	2 Federal income tax withheld $204.00
c Employer's name, address, and ZIP code			3 Social security wages $6,760.00	4 Social security tax withheld $419.12
Top Notch Manufacturing Co.			5 Medicare wages and tips $6,760.00	6 Medicare tax withheld $ 98.02
351 North Avenue Merrill, Wi 54452			7 Social security tips	8 Allocated tips
d Employee's social security number (your #)			9 Advance EIC payment	10 Dependent care benefits
e Employee's name, address, and ZIP code			11 Nonqualified plans	12 Benefits included in box 1
Your name Your address Your city and state zip code			13	14 Other
			15 Statutory employee ☐ Deceased ☐ Pension plan ☐ Legal rep. ☐ Deferred compensation ☐	
16 State Employer's state I.D. no.	17 State wages, tips, etc.	18 State income tax	19 Locality name 20 Local wages, tips, etc.	21 Local income tax

Department of the Treasury — Internal Revenue Service

Form **W-2** Wage and Tax Statement

LESSON 12. LABOR UNIONS

A labor union is made up of a group of workers who get together or organize so that they can deal with their concerns and problems at work. The union speaks for all of its members. Labor union members feel that they have more influence over conditions of their employment if they speak as a group, rather than if each worker talks with the employer alone.

The main purposes of the union are to get higher wages, improved working conditions, and fair treatment on the job for its members. It is easier for the union to get these things for the workers than if each individual tried to deal with the employer alone. It is much easier for an employer to replace one person than to replace all the people in the company. For example: If a worker is unhappy about wages, complaining to the employer might not help. The employer would probably find it easy to replace the individual with someone else. If all the employees complain about their wages, the employer may listen because it would be very difficult to replace all the workers. This is why unions have power and strength. When a group of workers and their employer talk about wages, hours, and working conditions, it is known as "collective bargaining." The whole idea of forming unions and taking part in collective bargaining is based on the fact that a group of people have more power and strength than one single worker when dealing with the employer.

The first unions in the United States were formed according to the kind of work a person did. A printer would join the printer's union and a carpenter would join a carpenter's union. Most of the trades or crafts in the United States had a union. These unions were known as "craft" (skill) or "trade" unions. In the late 1800's, all of the craft and trade unions joined together to form the American Federation of Labor (AFL).

As more and more factories hired workers in the United States, there was less need for skilled workers and a greater need for unskilled or semi-skilled workers. Many workers felt that it was necessary to form unions by industry, rather than by trade or craft. This was the start of the industrial union.   All the workers who worked in the steel industry joined a steel workers' union, while all the people in the automobile industry joined an automobile union, and so on. Later, all these industrial unions joined together to form the Congress of Industrial Organization (CIO).

In 1955, the American Federation of Labor (AFL) and the Congress of Industrial Organization (CIO) joined together to form the AFL-CIO. Some unions have left the AFL-CIO and are known as "independent unions." Two examples of independent unions are the United Mine Workers of America and the Teamsters.

Labor unions are organizations which are run for the benefit of the members. Union members elect officers who run the union. Members can attend monthly meetings of their union and take part in making decisions. Monthly dues are collected from members so that the union will have money for its activities.

Labor unions use a number of methods to get the things they want for their members. These methods include the following:

1. Collective Bargaining

In collective bargaining, the union, who represents the total group of workers, meets with the employer instead of each worker meeting alone with the employer. The union bargains, or negotiates, over wages and other conditions of employment for the members of the union. After the union and the employer agree, the terms or agreements are written in a contract called a "collective-bargaining contract" or "agreement."

Collective bargaining agreements cover such items as the following:

    A.   Wages - The amount the worker will be paid per hour or per week.

    B.   Working hours - The time the worker is expected to be on the job.

    C.   Premium pay - An additional amount of pay for work beyond the normal workday. For example, working more than the normal 40 hours per week; or working nights instead of the normal daytime hours.

    D.   Seniority rights - Rights earned by workers based on the length of time they have worked on the job. Seniority may be used to determine which worker will get a promotion to a better job or who gets laid off first when the employer has no work available.

    E.   Job security - Protects workers from the loss of their job because of things such as sickness or old age.

F. Pensions - The amount of money the person will receive at retirement.

G. Clean-up time - The amount of time the employee has for personal cleaning and changing clothes.

H. Vacations - The number of days of vacation with or without pay that are given per year.

I. Holiday pay - The number of holidays with or without pay that are given per year.

J. Union Shop - A worker does not have to belong to a union to be hired, but that person must join the union within a period of time (usually within 30 days) or lose the job.

K. Union dues deductions - The employer agrees to deduct union dues from the worker's earnings and pay the dues to the union.

L. Grievance procedure - The way disputes between the workers and their employer are settled. Disputes can arise over the meaning of language in the collective bargaining contract. Workers may also feel that they have been treated unfairly by the employer.

2. Strikes

A strike is a group of workers withholding their labor from the employer for a period of time. Strikes take place only after the workers vote by secret ballot to do so. The strike is one way the union tries to put pressure on the employer to gain more benefits. During the strike, the employer cannot make a product for sale. The worker gets no pay during the strike. Some unions have a strike fund. This fund gives money to striking members.

Most of the time during a strike there is picketing. Picketing is walking in front of the employer's place of business carrying signs. One reason for picketing with signs is to let everyone know a strike is going on. The other reason for picketing is to try to prevent the employer from replacing the workers on strike with other non-union workers. People who take jobs during a strike are called strikebreakers or "scabs".

3. Political action

Labor unions try to get federal, state, and local law-making bodies in the United States to pass laws which will help workers. Unions have played an important part in getting the Congress of the United States to pass laws for minimum wages, unemployment insurance, and health and safety standards.

Labor unions also take part in the election of government officials. Many times they give money to candidates who support the programs of labor unions. The money is used to help these candidates get elected to office.

Workers and employers do not always look at things in the same way. A wage increase, for example, is looked at by workers as something good because it will give them more money to spend at the grocery store. The employer, on the other hand, may not like a wage increase because it will add to the cost of doing business and may lower profits. Collective bargaining is one way that differences between workers and employers can be settled.

MATCHING: Match the words in Column 1 with the correct meaning in Column 2.

	Column 1		Column 2
_____	1. union	A.	not trained; not an expert
_____	2. collective	B.	protection against loss
_____	3. bargain	C.	as a group; all taken together
_____	4. craft	D.	a real or imagined wrong; reason for being angry
_____	5. unskilled	E.	trade that requires skilled work
_____	6. semi-skilled	F.	an agreement where two or more people agree to do a certain thing
_____	7. contract	G.	people walking around a factory to keep people from work
_____	8. security	H.	a group of workers joined together to promote their interests
_____	9. seniority	I.	an additional amount of pay for work beyond normal
_____	10. pension	J.	try to get good terms; to talk to reach an agreement
_____	11. grievance	K.	not belonging to a union
_____	12. non-union	L.	someone running for a public office
_____	13. strike	M.	having more training or skill than an unskilled worker
_____	14. picketing	N.	working on the job for a long period of time
_____	15. premium pay	O.	payment to person after retirement
_____	16. candidate	P.	stop work to get better pay, etc.

TRUE or FALSE: Place a "T" for true and an "F" for false before each statement:

_____ 1. The first unions in the United States were craft unions.

_____ 2. The craft and trade unions joined together to form the CIO.

_____ 3. The industrial unions joined together to form the AFL.

_____ 4. Workers and employers always look at things the same way.

_____ 5. The United Mine Workers of America is an independent union.

(continued)

_____   6.   A collective bargaining contract is an agreement between the employer and the union.

_____   7.   Bargaining and negotiating mean about the same thing.

_____   8.   Premium pay for work beyond the normal is usually a part of a collective bargaining contract.

_____   9.   Unions are concerned about the welfare of workers.

_____   10.   Non-union members may be hired in a union shop.

_____   11.   The employer pays the worker while the worker is out on strike.

_____   12.   Picketing is common during a strike.

_____   13.   Unions never give money to candidates for public office.

_____   14.   Membership in a union is free.

_____   15.   Labor unions try to get laws passed that help workers.

MULTIPLE CHOICE: Select the one best answer.

_____   1.   A strikebreaker is sometimes called

    a.   a scab   b.   a grievance   c.   a picket

_____   2.   Walking in front of a company during a strike is called

    a.   an open shop   b.   a union shop   c.   picketing

_____   3.   Disputes between a worker and employer are solved through

    a.   a job security check
    b.   a grievance procedure
    c.   union dues deductions

_____   4.   The first union of steel workers was a

    a.   craft union   b.   trade union   c.   industrial union

_____   5.   Talks about pay between the employer and the union are called

    a.   collective bargaining   b.   independent talk   c.   a boycott

_____   6.   In the early days, members of craft unions were

    a.   skilled workers   b.   unskilled workers   c.   semiskilled workers

_____   7.   A collective bargaining contract is also called

    a.   picketing   b.   a pension contract   c.   an agreement

_____   8.   A worker who has been with a company for a long time has many

    a.   negotiating rights   b.   seniority rights   c.   premium rights

_____   9.   Sometimes striking union members get money from

    a.   the employer   b.   a strike fund   c.   the government

_____   10.   In the late 1800's, the craft and trade unions joined together to form the

    a.   AFL   b.   CIO   c.   AFL-CIO

PLACES and JOBS:

Column 1 indicates places where people work. In Column 2 are names of jobs people would have in these places of work. Match Column 1 with Column 2.

<u>Column 1</u>

_____ 1.   drug store
_____ 2.   hospital
_____ 3.   animal hospital
_____ 4.   church
_____ 5.   post office
_____ 6.   business office
_____ 7.   meat market
_____ 8.   forest
_____ 9.   jewelry store
_____ 10. print shop
_____ 11. motel
_____ 12. beauty shop
_____ 13. window factory
_____ 14. interior decorator
_____ 15. home construction
_____ 16. railroad train
_____ 17. newspaper office
_____ 18. music store
_____ 19. automobile plant
_____ 20. restaurant
_____ 21. airplane
_____ 22. school
_____ 23. golf course
_____ 24. vegetable farm
_____ 25. insurance company

<u>Column 2</u>

A.   secretary
B.   clergyman
C.   hairdresser
D.   meat cutter
E.   piano tuner
F.   maid
G.   assembler
H.   paperhanger
I.   watch repairperson
J.   pharmacist
K.   pressman
L.   postal clerk
M. glazier
N.   nurses' aide
O.   reporter
P.   chain saw operator
Q.   cook
R.   veterinarian
S.   conductor
T.   plasterer
U.   lettuce picker
V.   turf technician
W. pilot
X.   policy writer
Y.   teacher

MATCHING UNIONS: In Column 1 is a list of the largest unions in the United States. In Column 2 is a list of the workers who would belong to these unions. Match Column 1 with Column 2.

Column 1

_____ 1. International Brotherhood of Teamsters

_____ 2. United Automobile Workers of America

_____ 3. United Steel Workers of America

_____ 4. American Federation of State, County, and Municipal Employees

_____ 5. Service Employees Union

_____ 6. International Ladies Garment Workers Union

_____ 7. United Mine Workers Union

_____ 8. International Brotherhood of Electrical Workers

_____ 9. Hotel and Restaurant Workers Union

_____ 10. United Paperworkers International Union

_____ 11. United Food and Commercial Workers

_____ 12. International Association of Machinists

Column 2

A. car assembly worker

B. public library worker

C. coal shaft worker

D. truck driver

E. seamstress

F. motor tester

G. sausage maker

H. lathe operator

I. maid

J. wood sorter

K. pig iron worker

L. nurses' aide

PREFIXES and SUFFIXES:

A syllable placed in front of a root word to change the meaning of a root word is called a prefix. A syllable added at the end of a root word is called a suffix.

Draw a single line under each prefix, and a double line under each suffix in the following words.

Examples: reread   movement   returned

1. replace

2. unskilled

3. semiskilled

4. non-union

5. worker

6. talked

7. government

8. treatment

9. improve

10. independent

11. agreement

12. workable

13. deduction

14. unsolved

15. disagreement

16. unfriendly

17. unemployment

18. joined

Skilled, Semiskilled, and Unskilled Workers.

An unskilled job is one that does not require any special training. Many times, these jobs require much physical labor. Unskilled work would be found in those occupations that require much walking or lifting. Many people are able to do unskilled work. Unskilled work generally pays the smallest wages since it does not require much training or ability. Many times, people who work in unskilled occupations find themselves out of work because they can be replaced by a machine that can do the same work. Examples of unskilled jobs would be ditch diggers, messengers, stable helpers, and car wash workers.

Semiskilled workers need some training, but the training generally does not take a long time. Sometimes the pay for semiskilled workers is good and sometimes it is not. It depends on the place where the person works. Sometimes semiskilled workers have a strong union and receive very good pay. Examples of semiskilled jobs are janitors, salesclerks, and car assembly workers.

Skilled work requires much training and experience on the job. Skilled workers usually get very good pay. It may take from two to eight years to get enough training and experience to become a skilled worker. There are fewer skilled workers because it takes much time and effort to get the necessary skill for this type of work. Examples of skilled jobs are typists and masons.

MANUAL OCCUPATIONS:

In the following list place a letter "S" before skilled jobs; place the letters "SS" before those that are semiskilled; and the letter "U" before those that are unskilled.

_____	1.	grocery carry-out	_____	8. lathe operator
_____	2.	dishwasher	_____	9. typesetters
_____	3.	painter	_____	10. custodian's helper
_____	4.	carpenter	_____	11. electrician
_____	5.	garbage collector	_____	12. cement worker
_____	6.	plumber	_____	13. bricklayer
_____	7.	fruit picker	_____	14. bus driver

TYPES OF JOBS: Following is a list of kinds of work employees must do on their jobs. Place the kind of work under the proper job.

1. checks doors and windows

2. arranges materials alphabetically

3. cleans water tanks

4. cleans vegetables

5. staples papers

6. keeps playground equipment in repair

7. mends fences

8. makes sandwiches

9. trims bushes

10. checks for fire

11. waters cattle

12. measures and mixes foods

13. operates elevator

14. files papers

15. brands cattle

16. feeds fish

17. stirs food

18. cleans swimming pool

19. checks cards of visitors

20. cares for fish equipment

21. checks water temperature

22. sorts papers and cards

23. cleans barns

24. mows lawns

Cattle Rancher

1. _____

2. _____

3. _____

4. _____

Night Watchperson

1. _____

2. _____

3. _____

4. _____

Filing Clerk

1. _____

2. _____

3. _____

4. _____

Fish Hatchery Worker

1. _____

2. _____

3. _____

4. _____

(continued)

TYPES OF JOBS: continued

Kitchen Helper   Playground Assistant

1. _____   1. _____

2. _____   2. _____

3. _____   3. _____

4. _____   4. _____

SPELLING: Correct the misspelled words.

1. purpuses   _____   9. bargians   _____

2. condtions   _____   10. senorty   _____

3. singel   _____   11. dedection _____

4. probebly   _____   12. chioce   _____

5. complaen   _____   13. canot   _____

6. industey   _____   14. disput   _____

7. milion   _____   15. pickut   _____

8. skiled   _____   16. goverment _____

MISSING LETTERS: Place the missing letter or letters in the blank spaces.

1. l __ bor   6. str __ ng __ h   11. pen __ ions

2. or __ an __ ze   7. sk __ __ led   12. ho __ id __ y

3. min __ mum   8. in __ ust __ ial   13. du __ s

4. col __ ec __ ive 9. to __ ether   14. de __ uct

5. neg __ tiates   10. co __ tra __ t   15. of __ ic __ al

(continued)

16. pick __ t

17. cand __ dat __ s

18. prof __ ts

19. un __ on

20. gen __ ral

21. e __ uipme __ t

22. gro __ ery

23. sec __ rity

24. grie __ ance

25. agre __ m __ nt

26. ass __ __ bly

27. jan __ tor

28. tea __ ster

29. me __ ber

30. proce __ ure

31. intern __ tional

32. phy __ ical

33. se __ ior __ ty

34. pr __ duct

35. disp __ t __

36. el __ ct __ d

QUESTIONS AND PROBLEMS:

1. Why does a labor union have power and strength?

2. What is an independent union?

3. List six items generally covered in a collective bargaining contract.

   A. _____   D. _____

   B. _____   E. _____

   C. _____   F. _____

4. Why do unions strike?

5. What is a union shop?

6. Why are unions active in politics?

LESSON 13.   FRINGE BENEFITS

Fringe benefits are the advantages or extras that a person gets on the job in addition to the regular wage or salary. Although some fringe benefits may not increase the amount of money a worker takes home, they are a very important part of what a person earns. Fringe benefits provided by the employer will provide some things that the employee will not need to buy from someone else.

On a job where there is a work or union contract, these fringe benefits are listed in the contract. On jobs where there is no union, the employer usually has a list of the fringe benefits that are available to the worker.

When a person hunts for a job, he/she should give as much attention to the fringe benefits as he/she does to the wages or salary. Two companies that pay the same wages may not give equal fringe benefits. Many things that are offered as fringe benefits are extras that the average worker may want. If the worker does not get them as fringe benefits, he/she may have to buy them with the money from his/her earnings.

There are three benefits that are given to nearly all workers. They are the following:

1. Social Security

Social Security benefits are paid to workers when they retire or become disabled. They are also paid to a worker's family in case of death. One-half of the cost of Social Security is paid by the employer and one-half by the worker. The worker's share is deducted from his/her gross or total earnings.

2. Unemployment Compensation Insurance

Unemployment compensation is money that will be paid if the worker loses a job and is unable to find another one. There is a limit to the amount of money the worker can receive, and the length of time it will be paid. Each state in the United States has its own Unemployment Compensation Laws. No two states have exactly the same laws.

In most states the cost of the unemployment compensation is paid by a direct tax on the employer. In these states, the worker does not pay any of the cost of the insurance because the employer pays it all. But some states tax the employee as well as the employer. In these states, the worker's share of the cost is deducted from his/her earnings.

Not all companies and employers are required to carry unemployment insurance. If the employer does not carry unemployment insurance, the worker will not receive money if he/she loses a job. Since the state laws vary, it is a good idea to know the law in the state where a person works.

3. Workmen's Compensation

Workmen's compensation is money that is paid to workers if they are injured or suffer illness because of their jobs. It is important to remember that the illness or injury must be caused by the job. For example, a person who cuts a hand on a table saw at work would have his/her doctor and hospital bills paid. A weekly check would be paid until the worker was well enough to return to work. A person getting sick with the flu while on the job would not receive money from workmen's compensation. In this case, the illness was not caused by the work.

The cost of workmen's compensation is paid by the employer. The employer pays into a state fund. Payments to injured workers are made from this fund. Some employers buy workmen's compensation insurance from private insurance companies and benefits are paid to injured workers by the insurance company.

If the worker dies because of a job injury or job-caused illness, money benefits are paid to the dependents. These payments are generally in addition to the Social Security benefits the dependents receive from the government.

In addition to the three benefits that most employers provide, there are many other benefits that the employer may make available to the worker. These include the following:

1.   Time Off

Some employers give time off with pay for many reasons. Some give time off with pay for some reasons and not for other reasons. A few employers give no time off with pay. Another employer may give neither vacation nor holidays with pay. The length of time allowed for vacation each year usually depends on how long the person has worked for the company. For example, the first year on the job, the worker may get only one week of vacation, while after ten years, the vacation may be extended to three weeks.

The holidays that employees usually are given are New Year's Day, Memorial Day, Fourth of July, Labor Day, Thanksgiving Day, and Christmas Day. Additional holidays, such as President's Day or Veteran's Day, may be allowed by some employers.

Some employers may also give time off with pay so that the employee may attend funerals or take part in military training. The worker may also receive a certain number of days off if there is a serious illness in the family.

If the worker gets sick and cannot work, many companies pay sick leave. Some companies may give five days of sick leave per year, while others may give seven or ten days. If workers do not use all of the sick days during the year, they may build up so that more days off would be available in future years. For example, an employer may give ten days sick leave per year. If the employee is not sick any days of the first year, twenty days would be allowed the second year. In some companies, the worker can build up as many as one hundred and twenty sick days if he/she works a long time for the company.

Time off with pay is an important fringe benefit. It could make a big difference in the worker's earnings during his/her lifetime.

2.   Insurance

Probably the most common type of insurance fringe benefit is hospital and medical insurance. This insurance pays doctor and hospital bills if workers or their dependents are ill or injured. The payment the employer or employee makes is called a "premium". Some companies pay all of the insurance premium. Other companies pay a part of the premium and the employee pays a part. The worker's part will be deducted from earnings. Hospital and medical insurance is an important fringe benefit because if it is not provided by the company, the employee will have to buy it. Today doctor and hospital costs are very high. It is important that everyone has some type of hospital and medical insurance.

During the past few years, many employers have allowed workers to buy term life insurance in a group policy. This life insurance pays money to the worker's family in case of death. The amount of life insurance can vary from one thousand ($1,000) to ten thousand ($10,000) dollars or it can be equal to the amount of the employee's yearly salary. The cost of group term life insurance is low. Some employers pay all of the premium. If the company pays only a part or none of the premium, the employee's payment will be deducted from his/her gross or total pay.

3.   Retirement Benefits

Many employers have some type of retirement program or pension plan for their employees. At the time of retirement, the worker receives a check each month in addition to a Social Security check. The amount of the pension check will depend on how long the employee has worked for the company. It will also depend on the amount that has been placed in the retirement fund. Some companies pay the whole cost of the pension plan, while in other companies, both the company and the worker each pay a part. When the employee pays a part of the cost, it is deducted from his/her earnings.

4.   Extra Pay

In addition to the regular wages that workers receive, the employer may pay more for certain kinds of work. If employees work more than the regular number of hours per week, they may be paid overtime pay. For example, workers who put in more than forty hours per week might receive time and one-half pay for all the hours over forty. If they are paid six ($6.00) dollars per hour regular pay, they would receive nine ($9.00) dollars per hour overtime pay.

Employees who work during the evening or during the night shift may receive more pay per hour than the person who works during the day. Companies that need workers on Saturday and Sunday may pay more than they do for weekday work. People who work on certain holidays may also receive extra pay.

Some employers also pay bonuses to employees. A bonus is an extra cash payment over the worker's regular wages. A bonus might be paid for very good work or for doing more on the job than is required. At times, an employer will pay a year-end or Christmas bonus. Sometimes this is the employer's Christmas present to the employees.

Extra pay can be an important item when considering fringe benefits. Sometimes extra pay can add many dollars to a person's regular paycheck.

5.   Discounts and Services

Sometimes when people work in stores, they are able to buy things at ten to twenty percent less than the store's customers pay. For example, people working in a clothing store may get ten ($10.00) dollars off when they buy a hundred ($100.00) dollar suit. Some restaurant workers get free meals, while others pay less than regular prices for their meals. Bus drivers may get free bus passes to go anywhere in the city.

Some companies provide certain safety clothing and equipment for employees. Other companies require that workers buy their own safety clothes and equipment. Certain companies operate cafeterias where employees may buy their own meals for less than regular prices. In other companies, the workers pay regular prices or carry their own lunch.

It is important to remember that fringe benefits are worth money. Just because they are not a part of a person's paycheck does not mean that they are worthless. Fringe benefits such as insurance, time off, pension benefits, extra pay, and discounts are important and worth money. Remember that when looking at a job, fringe benefits should be considered just as regular pay is considered.

The employer will usually explain the benefits available to the worker when he applies for a job. If the employer does not explain them, it is very important for the applicant to ask what fringe benefits are provided by the company. It may also be a good idea to compare the fringe benfits offered by different employers. Often times, these benefits are listed in the want-ads under the job offerings.

It should be remembered that in today's world, a person needs certain benefits and services. If the employer does not pay for all or part of these benefits or services, the worker may have to buy them from someone. The worker then pays all the cost. When this happens, the worker must spend some of his/her paycheck for these benefits or services. If they are supplied by the employer, the worker has gained a great deal, even if they are not a part of the regular pay.

MATCHING: Match the words in Column 1 with the best meaning from Column 2.

Column 1   Column 2

_____   1. fringe benefits   A.   money payment in case of loss, accident, or death

_____   2. offer   B.   let; permit

_____   3. equal   C.   usual; coming again and again at the same time

_____   4. unemployment   D.   extras over regular pay given for work

_____   5. compensation   E.   a regular payment to a person that is not wages

_____   6. insurance payment   F.   pay before deductions are taken off

_____   7. share   G.   given; to present something to a person

_____   8. vacation   H.   to take off a certain amount from the price

_____   9. holiday   I.   part belonging to a person

_____   10. premium   J.   person who buys something

_____   11. allow   K.   pay

_____   12. pension   L.   a day for pleasure and enjoyment

_____   13. gross pay   M.   the same in amount, size, number, or value

_____   14. regular   N.   time off from work

_____   15. bonus   O.   something extra over what is due; extra pay for doing good work

_____   16. discount   P.   having no job or work

_____   17. restaurant   Q.   cost of insurance

_____   18. customer   R.   place to buy and eat a meal

ORDER: Number the following sentences in the order in which they appeared in this lesson. The first one is done for you.

_____   1. The cost of workmen's compensation is paid by the employer.

_____   2. Some employers may also give time off with pay so that the employee may attend funerals or take part in military training.

_____   3. Many employers have some type of retirement program or pension plan for their employees.

___1___   4. Fringe benefits are the advantages or extras that a person gets on the job in addition to the regular wage or salary.

_____   5. People who work on certain holidays may also receive extra pay.

MATCHING BENEFITS: Match the benefit in Column 1 with the reason for the benefit in Column 2.

Column 1

_____ 1. workmen's compensation

_____ 2. unemployment compensation

_____ 3. Social Security

_____ 4. time off with pay

_____ 5. sick leave with pay

_____ 6. hospital insurance

_____ 7. life insurance

_____ 8. overtime pay

_____ 9. shift pay

_____ 10. year-end bonus

_____ 11. discount

_____ 12. pension

Column 2

A. worker has two weeks vacation

B. worker is in hospital with foot injured at home

C. worker cannot find a job after being laid off

D. employee cannot work because of a bad cold

E. employer gives fifty ($50) dollar gift to the employee

F. retirement check from the government

G. employee works during the night

H. worker pays less for shirt he buys

I. worker crushes foot in press while at work and cannot work

J. family receives money when worker dies

K. retirement check from company retirement plan

L. employee works sixty hours per week

MATCHING HOLIDAYS: Match the day in Column 1 with the reason the day is celebrated in Column 2.

Column 1

_____ 1. New Year's Day

_____ 2. Memorial Day

_____ 3. Fourth of July

_____ 4. Labor Day

_____ 5. Veteran's Day

_____ 6. Thanksgiving Day

_____ 7. Christmas Day

Column 2

A. giving thanks for blessings received

B. honor those who served in the military service

C. celebrate Jesus Christ's birthday anniversary

D. first day of the year

E. Independence of the United States

F. honor the dead

G. honor the American working person

BLANKS: Place the following words in the proper blank.

compensation   union   overtime
gross   vacation   bonus
regular   equal   deducted
premium

1.   Two companies that pay the same wages may not give _____ fringe benefits.

2.   On a job where there is a work or _____ contract, the fringe benefits are listed in the contract.

3.   The worker's share of Social Security is deducted from _____ or total earnings.

4.   The cost of workmen's _____ is paid by the employer.

5.   The length of time allowed for _____ each year usually depends on how long the worker has been employed by the company.

6.   Some companies pay the total cost of the life insurance _____ .

7.   When the employee pays part of the cost of the retirement program, it is _____ from his/her earnings.

8.   If employees work more than the regular number of hours per week, they may be paid _____ pay.

9.   A _____ might be paid for doing more on the job than is required.

10. When a person looks at a job, fringe benefits should be considered just as _____ pay is considered.

SPELLING: Correct the misspelled words.

1.   restauant   _____   11.   holadays   _____
2.   equipmet   _____   12.   adition   _____
3.   fring   _____   13.   pinsion   _____
4.   customars   _____   14.   medacil   _____
5.   precent   _____   15.   hosptal   _____
6.   certian   _____   16.   premuim   _____
7.   bonas   _____   17.   provid   _____
8.   presant   _____   18.   niether   _____
9.   fourty   _____   19.   enougf   _____
10. insurence   _____   20.   compensition   _____

TRUE or FALSE: Place a "T" for true and an "F" for false before each statement.

_____ 1. All companies pay the same fringe benefits.

_____ 2. Fringe benefits are an important part of a worker's earnings.

_____ 3. The employer pays all of the Social Security tax.

_____ 4. Unemployment compensation is exactly the same in all states of the United States.

_____ 5. Unemployment compensation is money paid to a worker who is injured on the job.

_____ 6. In all states, the employee pays a part of the cost of unemployment compensation.

_____ 7. There is no limit to the length of time a person can receive unemployment compensation.

_____ 8. A worker who gets the flu will receive workmen's compensation.

_____ 9. The cost of workmen's compensation is paid by the employer.

_____ 10. If a worker is injured on the job, doctor and hospital bills will be paid by workmen's compensation.

_____ 11. All employers give workers vacation with pay.

_____ 12. Many employers give sick leave with pay if the worker has the flu and cannot work.

_____ 13. Hospital and medical insurance pay doctor and medical bills for the worker and dependents.

_____ 14. Life insurance pays money to the worker's family in case of death.

_____ 15. The cost of group term life insurance is low.

_____ 16. All companies pay a Christmas bonus.

_____ 17. A worker who works the night shift might receive extra pay.

_____ 18. Overtime pay is the pay a worker receives for doing very good work.

_____ 19. A discount is when a worker can buy things from a store for less than the store's customers pay.

_____ 20. The employee always has to pay for safety equipment.

_____ 21. A worker who works more than forty hours per week may receive time and one-half pay for all the hours over forty.

_____ 22. The worker's share of Social Security is deducted from gross or total earnings.

TYPES OF JOBS: Following is a list of kinds of work employees must do on their jobs. Place the kind of work under the proper job.

1.	stock shelves	9.	cut boards	17.	mark lumber
2.	clean kitchen	10.	mark stock	18.	polish cars
3.	change tires	11.	pile 2 x 4's	19.	lift patients
4.	bathe patients	12.	clean cars	20.	clean streets
5.	unload lumber	13.	wash dishes	21.	make soup
6.	pave roads	14.	repair fences	22.	grease cars
7.	feed patients	15.	make beds	23.	wash pots and pans
8.	unload stock	16.	repair roads	24.	package merchandise

Service Station Attendant

1. _____

2. _____

3. _____

4. _____

Stock Clerk

1. _____

2. _____

3. _____

4. _____

Highway Worker

1. _____

2. _____

3. _____

4. _____

Lumber Yard Worker

1. _____

2. _____

3. _____

4. _____

Cook's Helper

1. _____

2. _____

3. _____

4. _____

Nurses' Aide

1. _____

2. _____

3. _____

4. _____

QUESTIONS and PROBLEMS:

1.   What is a fringe benefit?

2.   Why are fringe benefits important to the worker?

3.   List six fringe benefits.

  A. _____   D. _____

  B. _____   E. _____

  C. _____   F. _____

4.   List four reasons employees may get time off.

  A. _____   C. _____

  B. _____   D. _____

5.   List four reasons employees may get extra pay.

  A. _____   C. _____

  B. _____   D. _____

6.   An employee gets a twenty (20%) discount on merchandise purchased.
      What will an eighteen ($18.00) dollar sweater cost?

LESSON 14: JOB RESPONSIBILITIES

After finding employment, the next concern of the worker is to do his/her best and keep the job. The first month or two on a job can be very difficult. During the first month the worker may not know the job too well and may have many new things to learn. The worker may not know the boss and co-workers. Sometimes it is difficult for the new worker to know how to act on the job. Most employers will be understanding of anyone who tries to do good work. It is a mistake for the beginning worker to pretend to know it all.

There are a number of things that must be kept in mind if the worker wants to hold the job. Holding a job takes effort on the part of the worker. The points to be considered are the following:

1.   Learn the Job Quickly

A person is hired because the employer wants some service or work performed. It is important that the worker learn the duties quickly. By watching and listening carefully, the new employee will learn what to do. If he or she does not know what to do or how to do the job, it is best to ask someone. It is a mistake to pretend to know how to do the job if one does not know how to do it. Pretending may lead to more and bigger mistakes.

Asking the same question over and over again can get a person fired. The boss and co-workers will be glad to answer a question once or twice. They may not like it if it is asked again and again. The best rule would be for the worker to pay close attention so that the job can be learned quickly.

2.   Be Careful on the Job

Carelessness can get a worker fired from a job. Employers do not like employees who are careless. Carelessness could cause injury to the worker as well as to other workers. Many times poor work is the result of carelessness. It may slow down the rest of the workers as well as the careless person.

When workers do not know their jobs, they may not even know that they are careless.

Workers should know the job well and keep their minds on their work. Remember that employees are being paid to work and not to visit with friends or co-workers.

3.   Be Able to Accept Criticism

No one likes to be told that the job he/she has done is not good enough. The beginning worker may have to take a lot of criticism. When the worker accepts the criticism and tries to improve the work, it will be much easier to get along on the job.

Some workers get a "chip on the shoulder" or answer back when they are criticized. This can only lead to trouble with the boss or with co-workers. Remember that criticism is given to help the worker improve his/her working habits. If workers accept the criticism, they will be much happier on their jobs. As a worker's skills on the job improve, there will be less and less criticism.

4.   Be at Work Daily

Most people will be sick at some time during their working years. When workers are sick, they do not belong at work. They should be at home or in a hospital. There are also other reasons why people may miss work. They may have to attend a funeral, or they may have some other good reason. But the employer should know why the employee is taking time off. If the worker knows ahead of time that he/she will be gone on a certain date, he/she should tell the employer a few days before being absent.

Workers who do not have a good reason to be gone should be at work. Many times a missing worker upsets the whole working order of everyone on the job. Not only does the employer lose out because the work is not done, but the missed work may affect the other workers as well. For example, a plumber missing from a house-building job may prevent the plasterer from putting in the walls. The plumbing must be done before the walls can be plastered.

5.   Be on Time

When employers hire workers, they expect them to be on time. If the job starts at 7:30 a.m., the employee should be there at 7:30 or before. Many employers feel that people who are late for work really do not care about their jobs. It is foolish to lose a job because one is always five or ten minutes late. People who have trouble being on time should either get up earlier or plan their time better.

When employees find they will be late for some reason, they should call the boss as soon as possible. If they cannot call, they should explain the reason for being late as soon as they get to work. Being on time for school, for work, and for all of a person's appointments is a good habit to have.

6.   Follow Company Rules

Every employer has certain rules that the worker is expected to follow. Sometimes a rule may seem silly to the worker, but if he/she is just beginning to work with the company, he/she should follow the rules closely. When people start work for a company, they have the responsibility to find out what the rules are. When workers do not know or are not told the rules, they should ask. Sometimes there may not be a written rule, but the other employees may do things in a certain way. For example, there may not be a rule which states that a person should not go to the water fountain to get a drink more than once each hour, but no employee goes more often than this. The best way to learn the unwritten rules is to watch what other workers do. Remember that the new worker has much to learn the first few weeks on the job. The more he/she can learn, the better he/she will get along on the job.

7.   Be Courteous

The ability to get along with the boss and co-workers is one of the most important requirements on a job. The reason many people are fired from the job is that they cannot get along with other people. More people are fired for this reason than for any other reason. If a person wishes to get along with others, he must be courteous. Courtesy is treating others in a nice, polite way.

Workers should always remember that they should treat other workers and the boss the way they want to be treated. If they are courteous to others, they will find that most people will be courteous to them.

The worker should always try to be pleasant and cheerful. Most people would rather be around people who look at the good things in life. Many employees keep away from fellow workers who are always complaining about their work and everything else in life.

Sometimes workers may need to work next to someone they do not like. In this case, they will need to make a special effort to get along. A worker who wants to keep a job must learn to get along with many different kinds of people. Workers must get along with the boss and co-workers. At times this may not be easy, but it is very necessary. It is foolish to lose a job because of some little argument one might have with the boss or a co-worker.

8.   Be Responsible

Employers like workers they can depend on or count on to get the job done. These are the workers who the boss knows are going to do what they were hired to do. They are the people who are not looking for excuses to get out of work or do as little as possible.

Responsible workers do not raise a big fuss when something goes wrong. If this happens, they will just try their best to get the job done. Responsible persons are hard workers and are willing to do more than is absolutely necessary. They are the workers who do their share of the work and maybe a little more than their share. Such workers are more highly regarded by their employer.

Workers should work even if the boss or supervisor is not around. Good workers can work on their own. They do not need someone to tell them what to do all the time. So when responsible workers finish one job, they will start on another one. They do not wait for the employer to come back and tell them what to do. They use their heads and try to see what has to be done.

Responsible workers will also help other employees. They will never do things to get other workers into trouble with the employer. They will pay attention to their jobs and work to the best of their abilities. The dependable worker is not a show-off.

Employees are hired to do a job. If they are not responsible enough to get the job done, they may find themselves without employment. Being responsible is a good quality to have.

People who are responsible will find work more fun. People who are responsible may advance on the job much faster than people who are not responsible.

9.   Be Honest

There is no room for lying, cheating, or stealing on the job. A person who lies or cheats is not trusted by the boss or other people. Lying or cheating can give a person a "bad name" which may stay with him/her for a long time.

Employees should never take anything home with them from their jobs unless they have permission to do so. Taking something from a job without permission is a form of stealing. Even if the tool or article will be returned, taking or borrowing it does not make it right.

A worker should never steal anything from the employer or fellow workers. It is considered stealing even if the article taken is worth very little. There is no quicker way for a person to be fired from the job than to be caught stealing. Sometimes employers will overlook many weaknesses or faults in a worker, but very few will overlook stealing. Stealing is a crime and can lead to the loss of a job, a fine, or even a jail sentence.

10. Be proud of the job

Every worker should feel that his job is important. All honest work is important. It does not make any difference if one is a dishwasher, a plumber, a garbage collector, or a medical doctor. All of these occupations are necessary. They all provide a service or a product which can be used by others. A person who is a dishwasher should be just as proud of dishwashing as a medical doctor is of treating people.

People who are proud of their work will try to do a good job. People who are proud of their work will do the best job possible because they want to, and not because they have to. Being proud of one's work shows a good job attitude.

Holding a job takes effort. The more effort that workers put into their jobs, the better workers they will become. It is often said that people move up-the-job ladder because they are lucky. Sometimes this may be true, but usually the person who gets ahead is the hard worker who makes an effort to do his best.

11. Work Hard

Most work is not easy. Workers may be asked to do some things that they do not like to do. Being willing to accept work that is not enjoyed shows the employer that one is a good employee. Nearly all workers find that certain parts of their jobs are not enjoyable. Workers must learn to accept the undesirable tasks just as they accept the desirable tasks.

It has been said that if a job were always easy so many workers would want it that it would not pay any wages. The best rule to follow is to put in a full day's work for a full day's pay.

MATCHING: Match the words in Column 1 with the correct meaning in Column 2.

	Column 1		Column 2
_____	1. difficult	A.	finding fault with someone or something
_____	2. co-worker	B.	something that has been done
_____	3. effort	C.	not present; to be gone; to be away
_____	4. performed	D.	discussion by persons who disagree
_____	5. careless	E.	custom; usual practice; doing over and over
_____	6. criticism	F.	thinking well of oneself or being satisfied with oneself
_____	7. improve	G.	person who works with another person
_____	8. absent	H.	make better
_____	9. upset	I.	not watching what one does; not caring
_____	10. plaster	J.	to trick someone; to do business that is not honest
_____	11. habit	K.	great disorder; disturb
_____	12. unwritten	L.	not telling the truth
_____	13. courtesy	M.	hard to do or understand
_____	14. pleasant	N.	polite behavior; being kind
_____	15. cheerful	O.	easy to get along with; friendly; one who pleases
_____	16. argument	P.	joyful; glad
_____	17. responsible	Q.	try hard to do something
_____	18. cheat	R.	mixture of lime, sand, and water for covering a wall
_____	19. lying	S.	not written
_____	20. proud	T.	trustworthy; reliable; dependable

TRUE or FALSE: Place a "T" for true and an "F" for false before each statement.

_____   1.   A beginning worker has many things to learn when starting a new job.

_____   2.   It is important that a new worker learn the job as quickly as possible.

_____   3.   Pretending to "know it all" is a good job attitude.

(continued)

_____ 4. Asking the same questions again and again is a good way to get along on the job.

_____ 5. A careless person can slow down the work of other workers.

_____ 6. A worker should spend as much time as possible visiting with friends or co-workers.

_____ 7. A worker should get angry when criticized.

_____ 8. The criticism given should be used to improve the employee's working habits.

_____ 9. A worker should never miss work for any reason.

_____ 10. It does not make much difference if a person is five minutes late for work.

_____ 11. If workers miss work, they should let the boss know why they are missing.

_____ 12. Being on time for work is a good habit to have.

_____ 13. A worker does not have to follow the unwritten rules in a factory.

_____ 14. People can be fired from jobs if they do not get along with their co-workers.

_____ 15. Complaining about the boss is a good job attitude.

_____ 16. A courteous person teases fellow workers.

_____ 17. A dependable person is always looking for a way to get out of work.

_____ 18. Responsible workers raise a big fuss if they do not get their way.

_____ 19. Responsible workers do their share of the work and sometimes more than their share.

_____ 20. A person can be fired for stealing a small wrench from the shop where he/she works.

ALPHABETICAL ORDER: Place the following words in alphabetical (ABC) order.

1. careless   1. _____

2. care   2. _____

3. carelessness   3. _____

4. careful   4. _____

5. carefully   5. _____

6. carefree   6. _____

7. carefulness   7. _____

8. caretaker   8. _____

9. career   9. _____

JOB ATTITUDES: The following list of things tells about either a poor worker or a good worker. Place a "P" before a statement that tells about a <u>poor</u> worker. Place a "G" before a statement that tells about a <u>good</u> worker.

_____	1. does one's best	_____	26. is a happy person
_____	2. works hard	_____	27. is courteous
_____	3. is often absent	_____	28. listens to directions
_____	4. has poor manners	_____	29. tells dirty jokes
_____	5. is pleasant	_____	30. finishes work on time
_____	6. talks too much	_____	31. gossips about others
_____	7. is responsible	_____	32. likes to argue
_____	8. is a clock-watcher	_____	33. is proud of the work done
_____	9. is cheerful	_____	34. is a troublemaker
_____	10. takes criticism	_____	35. leaves work early
_____	11. becomes angry easily	_____	36. takes long work breaks
_____	12. is not neat	_____	37. is interested in work
_____	13. keeps busy	_____	38. keeps work area clean
_____	14. does extra work	_____	39. does as little as possible
_____	15. is a fault-finder	_____	40. is the clown in the factory
_____	16. is willing to learn	_____	41. teases other workers
_____	17. plays jokes on other workers	_____	42. has a quick temper
_____	18. keeps tools neat and clean	_____	43. is careless
_____	19. is messy	_____	44. gives praise to others
_____	20. dresses correctly	_____	45. is helpful to others
_____	21. laughs at mistakes of others	_____	46. shows off
_____	22. obeys rules	_____	47. does not follow orders
_____	23. keeps his mind on the work	_____	48. gives excuses
_____	24. complains about other workers	_____	49. never steals
_____	25. follows safety rules	_____	50. does not do fair share

SENTENCE ORDER: Number the following sentences in the order in which they appeared in this lesson. (The first one is done for you.)

_____ A worker should never steal anything from the employer or fellow workers.

_____ People who are proud of their work will do the best job possible because they want to, and not because they have to.

_____ When people start work for a company, it is their responsibility to find out what the rules are.

_____ Employers do not like employees who are careless.

_____ The beginning worker may have to take a lot of criticism.

_____ Many times a missing worker upsets the whole working order of everyone on the job.

__1__ It is important that the worker learn the duties quickly.

_____ Many employers feel that people who are late for work really do not care about their jobs.

_____ Workers should always remember that they should treat other workers and the boss the way they want to be treated.

_____ Good workers can work on their own.

BLANKS: Use one of the following words to fill in the missing words in the sentences below.

unwritten	difficult	carelessness	courtesy
proud	criticism	cheating	pleasant
habit	effort		

1. Sometimes it is _____ for the new worker to know how to act on the job.

2. Holding a job takes _____ on the part of the worker.

3. _____ can get a worker fired from a job.

4. As the worker's skills on the job improve, there will be less and less _____ given.

5. Being on time for school, for work, and for all of a person's appointments is a good _____ to have.

6. The best way to learn _____ rules is to watch what other workers do.

7. _____ is treating people in a nice, polite way.

8. The worker should always try to be _____ and cheerful.

9. Lying and _____ can give a person a "bad name."

10. People who are _____ of their work will try to do a good job.

MATCHING OCCUPATIONS: Below are some job titles and what the workers do on the job. Match the job with the work.

_____	1. dairy farm worker	A.	collects tickets
_____	2. messenger	B.	cares for horses
_____	3. waitress	C.	serves food
_____	4. forestry worker	D.	sets fish traps
_____	5. bellhop	E.	vacuums floors
_____	6. barber shop helper	F.	bottles milk
_____	7. park helper	G.	greases pans
_____	8. usher	H.	wraps packages
_____	9. parking lot attendant	I.	runs errands
_____	10. typist	J.	pumps gas
_____	11. janitor	K.	arranges papers alphabetically
_____	12. filing clerk	L.	cleans tables
_____	13. store clerk	M.	plants seedlings
_____	14. construction worker	N.	packages meat
_____	15. fisherman	O.	types papers
_____	16. bakery worker	P.	paves streets
_____	17. nurses' aide	Q.	carries baggage
_____	18. painter's helper	R.	milks cows
_____	19. riding stable helper	S.	paints stables
_____	20. service station worker	T.	parks cars
_____	21. grocery store worker	U.	shines shoes
_____	22. road worker	V.	marks cans
_____	23. bus boy	W.	lifts patients
_____	24. butcher	X.	corrects papers
_____	25. dairy products worker	Y.	hauls concrete
_____	26. teacher	Z.	mows lawns

QUESTIONS AND PROBLEMS:

1. If a person wants to hold a job, list ten points that should be considered.

    A. _____   F. _____

    B. _____   G. _____

    C. _____   H. _____

    D. _____   I. _____

    E. _____   J. _____

2. Why should one try to learn the job quickly?

3. How can criticism help a worker?

4. Why should the worker try to be on time?

5. What is an unwritten rule?

6. Why should a worker show pride in work?

7. Explain what "chip on the shoulder" means.